TROUBLE
in the
THIRD KINGDOM

TROUBLE
in the
THIRD KINGDOM

The Minerals Industry in Transition

by

Simon D. Strauss

MINING JOURNAL BOOKS LIMITED
LONDON

Published 1986 by:
Mining Journal Books Ltd., 60 Worship Street,
London, EC2A 2HD, England.
© Mining Journal Books 1986.
ISBN 0 900117 41 9

Text set in 11/13 pt Times Medium Roman by photo-composition and printed offset litho by Chandlers (Printers) Ltd., Bexhill-on-Sea, East Sussex, England.

iv

Contents

List of Tables

List of Charts

Acknowledgements

This book represents observations based on almost 60 years of following the markets for minerals under widely varying circumstances — prosperity, depression, war, peace, inflation and deflation. As in all such endeavours it reflects experiences shared with others, knowledge absorbed from others and opinions influenced by others.

My father, Lester W. Strauss, a professional mining engineer with long experience in Latin America, Canada and the United States, first introduced me to the industry. Arthur W. Allen, the editor of *Engineering and Mining Journal,* was my first employer. William L. Clayton, who subsequently became Under Secretary of State in the United States, initiated me in the mysteries of major commodity negotiations.

The book itself has been written under the constant guidance and trenchant observation of the editorial director of Mining Journal Books Ltd, Michael West, whose patient and perceptive observations have kept me from wandering off the track.

The physical preparation of the manuscript has been facilitated by the unstinted labours of Billie Curtin, a secretary at the consulting firm of Behre, Dolbear & Company, Inc. I am grateful to the head of that firm, Hans W. Schreiber, for making her services available to me and also to Rose Ritter who assisted in the preparation of graphs.

To the World Bureau of Metal Statistics, the American Bureau of Metal Statistics, the U.S. Bureau of Mines and Metallgesellschaft I am indebted for access to their past records of mineral statistics.

Simon D. Strauss

Animal

Mineral

Vegetable

Trouble in the Third Kingdom

To children, these are the three kingdoms that encompass all objects. When playing guessing games, such as Twenty Questions, the first effort is to identify the kingdom within which lies the unknown correct answer.

The members of the animal and vegetable kingdoms are alive — they are organic. The non-fuel members of the mineral kingdom are lifeless — they are inorganic. This basic difference affects public perceptions in subtle ways. The subconscious reaction to animal and vegetable substances is positive. Frequently the reaction to minerals tends to be negative.

Organic substances reproduce. Depending on the surrounding environment they may be abundant or they may be relatively scarce. Ensuring the survival of rare species of animals and plants has become a public priority; regulations have been invoked to protect endangered species against the threat of hostile forces.

Inorganic substances — non-fuel minerals — are non-renewable. The quantities contained within the globe cannot be precisely measured but, as production increases, fears arise periodically that mineral resources may be exhausted. Should that occur, modern civilization would be adversely affected. Thus, dependence on minerals conveys threatening implications of insecurity.

Moreover, the physical acts involved in mining and processing of minerals disturb some people. Inevitably these acts involve environmental consequences. The earth's surface is changed as soil and rocks are removed to provide access to mineral deposits. Processing creates problems of air and water pollution and of disposal of waste

1

materials. Some minerals, ubiquitous within the earth's surface, have toxic properties. If dealt with unwisely, they may adversely affect public health.

The favourable public reactions to animals and vegetables are clearly evident in the multitudes of admiring observers who visit zoos and botanical gardens. Museums devoted to mineral specimens draw sparse attendance.

Typical of the negative attitude towards minerals is the critical letter written by a housewife to the manager of a Miami cinema. His programme had included a 10-minute short subject, *Challenge in the Earth,* detailing the history of a mining enterprise. She wrote that she could not understand why he chose to exhibit a film that glorified "the rape of the earth". In particular she objected to a scene showing a huge electric shovel loading broken rock into a mammoth off-highway truck.

In reply, she was informed that the broken rock was copper-silver ore being mined in Arizona. Without copper wire, the motion picture projector could not have operated. Without silver, no picture could have appeared on the screen. Moreover, the fire laws of Miami required that the theatre in which she sat be constructed primarily of mined materials rather than wood — flammable vegetable matter. If the earth was indeed being raped by the act of mining, the rape was being conducted in part to enable her and others to see motion pictures.

This ignorance of the essential role of minerals in daily life is not exceptional. In another example, a sophisticated organization of businessmen in San Diego was described, by its leaders, as having no real interest in the problems of assuring access to supplies of chrome and cobalt. A leading spokesman on the issue of U.S. import dependence had suggested this as a topic for an evening meeting. When told that his suggestion lacked relevance, he asked if it were not true that San Diego was an important defence base, that one of its leading industries was aircraft production, and that it was a major medical centre. When the reply was in the affirmative for all three, he pointed out that the production of equipment for defence, aviation and health care required cobalt and chrome.

Without minerals modern society would not exist. In all but the most primitive societies minerals enter into every aspect of daily life. They provide the basic framework of industrial production.

The world economy grew rapidly between the end of World War II and the year 1974. During this period world consumption of most minerals doubled or tripled over the volumes that had prevailed during and immediately after the war. In some cases — aluminium, for example — consumption grew ninefold.

The minerals industry of the world met all these requirements. It discovered and developed the necessary additional resources, disproving the theory of many that finite mineral resources were being rapidly exhausted. It raised the large sums required for investment in additional productive capacity. Thanks to productivity advances and technological progress it kept production costs within bounds. Prices of minerals remained in line with other goods and services.

Thus, the post-war years brought prosperity to the minerals industry — The Third Kingdom.

Yet now that Kingdom is in trouble.

Since 1974, after 30 years of rapidly expanding consumption, the rate of growth has perceptibly slowed for most minerals. In a few cases world consumption has actually declined.

Substantial over-capacity exists in many mineral commodities. In part, this is the consequence of new projects started prior to 1974 when markets were expanding but completed since then in a time of market stagnation.

Periods of sustained over-production have led to accumulations of excessive inventories. As a consequence, prices have been weak. For many minerals the level of prices has been unremunerative for most producers during recessionary periods.

Even when industrial growth has resumed and consumption has risen, with surplus inventories being reduced, prices have remained unsatisfactory.

Heavy financial losses were sustained by mineral producers during the severe recessions of 1975 and of 1981-82. Numerous mines and processing plants closed, workers lost their jobs, and the economies of entire regions have been undermined.

3

Governments of countries substantially dependent on mineral production as a major factor in their national economies have suffered adverse effects as tax revenues and earnings of foreign currencies from mineral exports have declined sharply.

The structure of the mineral industries was being transformed even before 1974. New countries had emerged as important centres of production, capturing market share from established producing nations. Control of mining enterprises had shifted. In many countries the host governments had formed public-sector companies to operate properties previously controlled by foreign investors. In other cases firms not previously experienced in non-fuel minerals operations had acquired substantial mining companies. The incursion of major petroleum companies into the United States' copper industry was a notable example of this trend.

With the altered status of the mineral industries since 1974 new managements faced baffling problems. For them and for the governments of mining countries, the markets appeared to be not only unpredictable but at times irrational.

This book endeavours to analyze the root causes of the changed outlook for the mineral markets. The point of view is that of one observer who has followed these markets since the late 1920s. Inevitably many will disagree with some or all of the interpretations and conclusions.

The subject is at once complex, fascinating and baffling. At any given time the market for a particular mineral is a composite not only of the basic elements of demand, supply, costs and prices, but also of the perceptions held by buyers and sellers as to the likely course of future events. While businessmen are prone to have firmly-held opinions about the future, the wise businessman will recognize that there are no certainties.

To begin with, some definitions are needed.

The industries covered are the non-fuel minerals — metallic and non-metallic. However, because of the leading role played by the energy crisis in recent economic history, necessarily this work contains some references to the fuel minerals — and particularly to the efforts to control oil prices.

4

In assessing the minerals trade, the first essential is to recognize the great differences between the market-economy countries and the countries with planned economies. In the first group economic decisions are made by individual enterprises; in the second group by central governments. In the first group, subject to some restraints of tariff and other barriers, minerals move freely in international trade. In the second group international trade occurs only to the extent that it is sanctioned by the state.

The market-economy countries are sub-divided into the developed and the developing nations. The countries of Western Europe, the United States, Japan, Canada, Australia and South Africa are heavily industrialized. The last three of this group are substantial exporters of many minerals. The other developed countries are net importers. These developed market-economy countries do not have completely unrestricted free trade. They resort to quotas, tariffs and other measures to protect certain segments of their industries — but, these barriers notwithstanding, the flow of mineral trade among them is of enormous proportions and their consumption of minerals in relation to their populations is large.

The developing countries, often referred to as the Third World, include the nations of Latin America, Africa (other than South Africa), Asia (other than Japan), and the Pacific Basin (other than Australia). Most of them are in the early stages of industrial development. Hence, their consumption of minerals is low in relation to their populations. However, in recent years a number of developing nations have succeeded in making significant gains in industrial output — notably Brazil, Mexico, India, the Republic of Korea and Taiwan. As a group, the developing nations are large exporters of minerals to developed nations.

The centrally-planned economy countries include the COMECON countries of Eastern Europe, the People's Republic of China, Cuba, Vietnam and Korea D.P.R. Yugoslavia's position is somewhat ambivalent. Its government is Socialist and exercises control over trade and industry, but for the past 30 years its trade orientation has largely been directed towards market-economy nations; it has observer status at COMECON.

5

For many minerals, based on the limited information available on their production and consumption, the centrally-planned countries appear to account for between one-quarter and one-fifth of global totals. Only a small portion, however, enters into trade with the market-economy countries. Chapter 9 amplifies this trade.

The text makes frequent reference to demand and consumption; and to supply and production. These words are not used interchangeably. Demand is used in the sense of total purchasing potential, whereas consumption refers to quantities actually converted into a processed product. In the same way supply is used in the sense of total selling potential, whereas production refers to the actual quantities of a mineral extracted in a given year.

To illustrate: at any given time, demand may exceed consumption by a substantial amount because (a) consumers may be adding to their stocks; (b) governments may be creating reserves of raw material feedstocks as a protection against future contingencies such as wars or shortages; or (c) speculators may be buying commodities in anticipation of higher prices. At other times demand may fall well below actual consumption because consumers are reducing inventories, governments are liquidating raw-material reserves, or speculators are selling in anticipation of lower prices.

An analogous relation exists between supply and production. Supplies will exceed production when consumers are destocking or governments are liquidating their reserve inventories or speculators are selling.

An added significant factor in the balance between supply and production in the case of minerals which can be recycled (chiefly the metals) is the volume of scrap being offered. Dealers in scrap may be heavily influenced by their price expectations — sometimes their offerings will be less than the volume of scrap being generated if they anticipate future price rises. If they anticipate lower prices they will sell all their existing stocks of scrap and perhaps take steps to generate more scrap by seeking out recoverable material from sources they do not ordinarily tap. Minerals recovered through ore extraction are referred to as primary production; minerals recovered through scrap recycling are referred to as secondary production.

A considerable array of weight measurements is used to measure mineral production and consumption — troy ounces, carats, avoirdupois pounds, flasks, piculs, short tons, long tons, and the metric system (grammes, kilogrammes and metric tons). In the interest of uniformity, except where specifically stated, the statistics in this volume are based on metric measurements. The metric system is being used increasingly in international trade. Unqualified, the term "ton" refers to the metric ton; where other units are used the full description is given.

Overall costs of mineral production break down between capital costs required to initiate production and operating costs required to maintain production.

Mineral industries are capital intensive. A new minerals project (sometimes referred to as a "green fields" project) requires investments of large sums and the lapse of considerable time between the decision to proceed and the actual inception of operations. Typically, mineral projects take two to five years for development and equipment once sufficient reserves have been outlined to justify proceeding with their construction.

During this period, no revenue is available. Thus, in addition to actual outlays for wages, equipment and materials of construction, a cost of money is incurred. This is true whether the project has been financed with equity funds or with borrowed money (recently most projects have involved both equity and debt).

After production begins, the outlays to cover the extraction, processing and transport of the product represent operating costs. If the revenues from sales exceed the operating costs, the project is said to generate a positive cash flow. But for a true profit to be realized, the revenues must also fully cover the capital costs. These include charges for depreciation and depletion (which represent amortization of the investment), interest on any debt, and a reasonable return on equity investment after income taxes have been covered.

The distinction between cash flow after covering operating costs and true net income after covering capital costs has acquired great significance in recent years. Under the stringent market conditions prevailing since 1974, many mines have continued to produce so long as they provide some cash flow. To the extent revenues do not cover capital costs, the project falls short of generating the funds needed to maintain production facilities in good condition, to undertake exploration to replace depleted deposits, to amortize debt, or to undertake new investments.

Costs per unit of marketable mineral produced are lowest when operations are at or close to capacity. Economies of scale can be realized by this procedure since some costs (capital costs, overhead, utility charges and other items) are relatively constant, regardless of the rate of operation. This means that mine operators have a strong incentive to maximize output even in periods of declining prices and lagging consumer buying.

Eventually, however, private-sector mineral producers cannot remain in business if sales revenues only cover immediate operating costs. With limited cash flow, they will be unable to finance exploration or capital investments in new properties to replace those they are depleting. Nor will a poor earnings record permit them to attract new funds in the capital markets. Inadequate profits are the reason that many long-established mining concerns, once leaders in the industry, have faded from the scene during the past 15 years.

The position of mineral enterprises controlled by public-sector corporations is different. Provided their governments are prepared to continue to channel funds from other revenues into the mineral enterprises, they will survive even with negative cash flows. In making decisions on investments, governments are influenced by such considerations as national security, maintenance of employment, foreign-currency earnings from mineral exports, or the desire to assist undeveloped regions of their countries. In the minds of government officials these considerations may outweigh adverse balances between revenues and costs.

From what has been stated, it is clear that the level of price is a pivotal factor in the economics of the mineral industries. Among the market-economy countries, the prevailing prices for a mineral are unlikely to be identical in all countries at any given time but they usually maintain a relationship of rough equilibrium. Efforts to hold prices in one market at a substantial premium or a substantial discount from prices in other markets eventually prove fruitless. After due allowance for transport costs, relevant tariffs, and other inhibiting factors, minerals are invariably attracted to the higher-priced market and away from the lower-priced market. As the trade flows change, equilibrium is restored among the principal markets.

Except for price controls imposed by government in wartime, efforts to control mineral prices have invariably failed in the market economies. It is a different story in the centrally-planned economies. There prices are set by government agencies. While black markets may exist in some consumer goods fields, industrial raw materials such as minerals are transferred from one government-owned enterprise to another at the quotations which have been officially set. Comparison with prices in the market-economy countries has little relevance, since in the centrally-planned countries prices are quoted in local currencies that are not freely convertible into other currencies. Most significant of all, imports of competitively priced foreign minerals are not permitted without government approval.

There is no completely satisfactory way to chart mineral price movements over extended periods of time. The best approximation appears to be to use prices quoted in the United States dollar, since this has been the currency most widely used in international trade during the post-war era. Most world statistics on imports and exports are stated in U.S. dollars. As the purchasing power of the dollar has fallen sharply over the years, price tabulations stated in current dollars provide a misleading impression of real trends. To get a true comparison, prices need to be restated in constant dollars.

Under classic economic theory, when demand for a commodity exceeds supply, the price rises to discourage consumption and to encourage production from marginal sources. Conversely, when supply exceeds demand for a commodity, the price falls to encourage consumption and to discourage marginal output.

These forces work sluggishly in the minerals industry. Demand for minerals is extremely sensitive to changes in the business cycle. It is influenced more by the level of economic activity than by the specific level of price. Supply is far less elastic. Time is required to bring marginal deposits into production. Once they are in operation, they may continue to produce even if demand is inadequate to absorb all supplies.

Thus, imbalances between demand for minerals and supply of minerals have a tendency to persist over extended periods of time. The consequence is that mineral prices may appear to be out of phase with average costs of production during such imbalances. In periods of shortage they rise far above costs; in periods of surplus they may persist at unremunerative levels.

The chapters that follow endeavour to illustrate the many factors that contribute to this unsatisfactory economic performance by a basic industry.

CHAPTER ONE

The Appetite for Minerals

The Paley Report Forecasts

"Consumption of almost all materials is expanding at compound rates and is thus pressing harder against resources which, whatever else they may be doing, are not similarly expanding. This materials problem is thus not the kind of 'shortage' problem, local and transient, which in the past has found its solution in price changes which have brought supply and demand back into balance. The terms of the materials problem we face today are larger and more pervasive."

The words sound ominous. They are the conclusions reached by the United States' President's Materials Policy Commission, better known as the Paley Commission, in its five-volume report to President Truman, published in 1951.

The Paley Commission was not the first to utter such warnings, and it has not been the last. In 1798 Thomas Malthus foresaw disaster for mankind because population was increasing by geometrical ratio and the means of subsistence by arithmetical ratio. In 1972 the Club of Rome concluded that depletion of the non-renewable resources of the globe — meaning the minerals — imposed severe limits to growth.

Yet in many ways the Paley Report was the most comprehensive and the timeliest of the many surveys of the prospective balance between global demand for materials and probable supply availability. It was comprehensive in that, based on 18 months of study, it dealt with all the major industrial commodities, excepting food. It was timely in that it came at mid-century, shortly after the end of the devastating Second World War. Its analysis projected both demand and supply for the subsequent 25 years — from 1950 to 1975. It analyzed each commodity within the market-economy world, excluding nations then under the control of socialist governments, the centrally-planned countries. That exclusion was due to inadequacy of statistical data. Within the market-economy nations, the Commission reported separate figures for the United States and for all other countries as a group.

The study emphasized the dominant role that the United States played in resource use. Opposite the first page of the text appeared a map of the world. On it were superimposed bar charts relating to consumption of petroleum, rubber, iron ore, manganese ore, zinc and copper. The caption read "U.S. Is Free World's Biggest Materials Consumer." A sub-heading pointed out that the United States had 9·5% of the population and 8% of the land area of the market-economy world. Yet the bars showed that, in 1950, the United States had consumed quantities roughly equal to the amounts consumed in all the other market-economy countries combined.

Five distinguished citizens comprised the Commission. Its chairman was William S. Paley, then chairman of the Columbia Broadcasting System. Staff work was done by experienced scientists, engineers, economists and writers, drawn largely from the U.S. Government. The facilities of all the relevant government agencies were made available — including the Geological Survey, the Bureau of Mines, the Forestry Service and the Bureau of Land Management. To obtain the views of the public on resource problems, the Commission interviewed leaders in industry and the academic world.

Regardless of the accuracy of its forecasts, the industry and zeal shown by the Commission deserve commendation. A mammoth and conscientious job was done in assembling and analyzing the data contained in the final voluminous report.

As the conclusions already cited indicate, the Paley Report anticipated substantial growth in the consumption of basic industrial materials during the third quarter of the century. Yet the reality far outran the anticipation. In most instances, use of specific minerals by the mid-70s was at least twice as great as the Paley study had predicted. The discrepancy was chiefly due to consumption in the countries other than the United States.

Having pointed out the disproportionate share of the world's industrial output accounted for by a single nation, the United States, the Paley Commission apparently assumed that this lop-sided relationship would persist throughout the third quarter of the century.

In a way, this was a curious assumption. In 1950 United States' industrial facilities were in excellent shape. World War II had caused massive expansion of U.S. heavy industry. No war damage had been sustained to U.S. plant facilities during the four fateful years of the war.

On the other hand, the chief industrial rivals of the United States among the market-economy nations had suffered enormous damage. Bombing raids had reduced many industrial plants in Britain, Japan, Germany, Italy and the rest of Western Europe to piles of rubble. By 1950 only limited reconstruction had begun.

To assist in that reconstruction of the war-shattered economies of its adversaries as well as its allies, the United States launched the Marshall Plan. By 1950 this generous aid programme had just begun to gather momentum.

Clearly the Commission did not foresee the extent to which the Marshall Plan, combined with the self-help zeal of the affected nations, would succeed. In the 25 year period covered by its forecasts great strides would be made in improving the living standards of these other nations to levels within striking distance of the high living standards in the United States. The progress made by the other developed nations is today clearly reflected in the prevalence of such consumer durable goods as automobiles, telephones, refrigerators and washing machines in the hands of their blue collar workers. In 1950 most of those workers were barely aware of the existence of such luxuries, much less anticipated possessing them.

Table 1 contrasts the Paley Commission estimates of consumption of nine key mineral commodities for the mid-seventies with actual consumption in the year 1973. The Paley Commission wanted to measure prospective demand for newly mined minerals, since these

TABLE 1: PALEY FORECASTS COMPARED WITH ACTUAL EXPERIENCE
(thousands of tons)

Mineral	(a) Consumption in 1950	(b) Paley Forecast for 1975	(c) Consumption in 1973	Comparisons (b)/(c) %	Comparisons (a)/(c) %
CONSUMPTION IN UNITED STATES					
Aluminium	835	3,265	6,165	+ 89	+ 738
Copper	1,140	1,635	1,725	+ 6	+ 51
Lead	710	1,090	805	− 26	+ 13
Tin	71	84	58	− 31	− 18
Zinc	980	1,350	1,350	0	+ 38
Chrome ore	890	1,780	1,270	− 29	+ 43
Iron ore	118,000	181,000	133,400	− 26	+ 13
Manganese ore	1,650	2,450	1,940	− 21	+ 18
Nickel	91	182	179	− 2	+ 97
CONSUMPTION IN OTHER MARKET-ECONOMY COUNTRIES					
Aluminium	423	2,175	5,800	+ 167	+1,271
Copper	1,175	1,860	4,725	+ 154	+ 302
Lead	785	1,360	2,070	+ 52	+ 164
Tin	73	109	154	+ 41	+ 111
Zinc	890	1,540	3,150	+ 105	+ 254
Chrome ore	615	1,120	3,760	+ 236	+ 511
Iron ore	93,500	150,000	482,600	+ 222	+ 416
Manganese ore	1,695	2,090	10,885	+ 421	+ 542
Nickel	29	58	295	+ 409	+ 917
AGGREGATE CONSUMPTION IN MARKET-ECONOMY COUNTRIES					
Aluminium	1,258	5,440	11,965	+ 120	+ 852
Copper	2,315	3,495	6,450	+ 85	+ 179
Lead	1,495	2,450	2,875	+ 17	+ 92
Tin	144	193	212	+ 10	+ 47
Zinc	1,870	2,890	4,500	+ 56	+ 141
Chrome ore	1,505	2,900	5,030	+ 73	+ 283
Iron ore	211,500	331,000	616,000	+ 86	+ 191
Manganese ore	3,345	4,540	12,825	+ 182	+ 283
Nickel	120	240	474	+ 98	+ 295

Comparison with 1975 Paley Forecast is actual consumption in 1973 for reasons discussed on page 13.

Source: Data on 1950 consumption and 1975 forecast from report of the Paley Commission. Consumption figures for 1973 from U.S. Bureau of Mines.

Note: Figures refer to consumption of primary material only; secondary material excluded.

involved the use (depletion) of non-renewable resources. This was the responsibility assigned to it by President Truman. Therefore, the figures are based on expected consumption of primary materials only — that is materials derived from newly mined sources. Secondary materials recovered through the recycling of scrap were excluded.

The Commission did not ignore the significant share of world consumption of minerals met by the recycling of scrap — and in fact increased recycling was one of its recommendations for lessening the drain on resources. But to judge how well prospective demand could be met, the Commission decided it had to assess the quantities of mineral that would have to be mined in the future.

The Commission's forecasts were for the specific year 1975, the last year of the quarter century. However, due to the energy crisis that developed in late 1973 and early 1974, world economic activity suffered a severe recession in 1975 — and, in fact, the business cycle had already turned down during the second half of 1974. Thus, it seems appropriate to contrast the Paley forecasts with the actual primary consumption in 1973. That year saw the highest demand of any year in the quarter century covered by the Paley study.

In line with the Paley format, Table 1 contains separate figures for 1973 consumption for minerals in the United States and in the rest of the market-economy countries.

Note that the Paley Report had estimated substantial global growth for each of the materials — ranging from a minimum of 34% for tin over the 25 year span to a maximum of 332% for aluminium. Also the report assumed that this growth would occur both in the United States and in the other Free World countries. In no case was a decline in consumption projected.

As already stated, the forecasts proved far too conservative. For most materials, global consumption in 1973 was at least double the amount that the Paley Report had forecast for 1975. The Commission had made its most optimistic estimate (up 332%) in the case of aluminium. In actuality aluminium consumption in 1973 was 852% greater than consumption in 1950. The average annual increase in use of aluminium on a world basis had been an astonishing 8% annually, compounded.

15

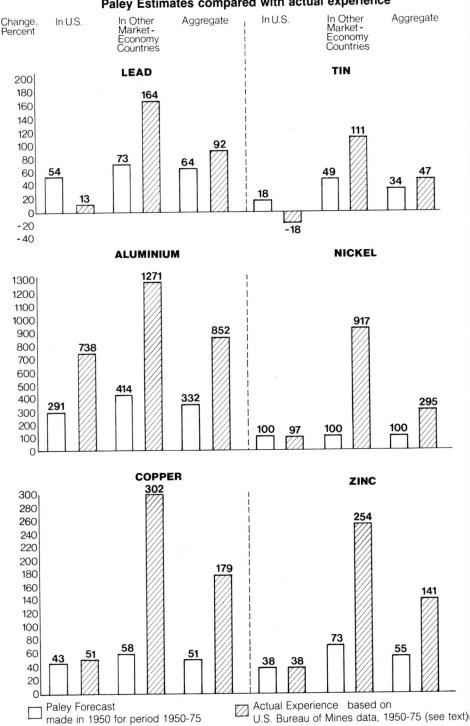

CHART 1. CONSUMPTION TRENDS DURING THE THIRD QUARTER OF THE CENTURY
Paley Estimates compared with actual experience

Change, Percent | In U.S. | In Other Market-Economy Countries | Aggregate | In U.S. | In Other Market-Economy Countries | Aggregate

LEAD

54, 13, 73, 164, 64, 92

TIN

18, -18, 49, 111, 34, 47

ALUMINIUM

291, 738, 414, 1271, 332, 852

NICKEL

100, 97, 100, 917, 100, 295

COPPER

43, 51, 58, 302, 51, 179

ZINC

38, 38, 73, 254, 55, 141

☐ Paley Forecast made in 1950 for period 1950-75

▨ Actual Experience based on U.S. Bureau of Mines data, 1950-75 (see text)

In only two cases — tin and lead — were the Paley estimates fairly close. Global tin consumption in 1973 was 10% greater than the Paley expectations; lead consumption was 17% greater.

But if one looks at the figures for the United States alone, the perspective is different. United States' consumption in 1973 of five commodities — lead, tin, manganese, chromite, and iron ore — fell below the Paley forecasts. In fact, the United States used less primary tin in 1973 than in 1950, the only decline from 1950 consumption shown in the entire tabulation.

Why did the United States lag behind?

The actual use of steel in the United States expanded during the period, but much of this consumption was met through imports of steel and of steel products, automobiles being a notable example. Consequently less iron ore, manganese and chromite were required in the United States than the Commission had estimated.

Moreover, a major shift occurred in the ferro-alloy business. Instead of importing manganese ore and chromite to produce ferro-manganese and ferro-chrome as in the past, increasingly the United States (with no viable domestic mine production of these two minerals) imported ferro-alloys rather than raw ores. The manganese and chromite figures in the table represent quantities of ore used rather than the end use of the element in whatever form. Various factors played a role in this shift — competitive costs, environmental controls in the United States that would have required heavy investment for modern ferro-alloy plants, and measures taken by the manganese and chromite mining countries to foster construction of their own facilities to produce ferro-alloys.

Thus, for three of the five commodities, the failure of U.S. consumption to attain the Paley estimates was primarily due to changes in the pattern of trade rather than to a lower level of ultimate use. But for the other two — tin and lead — actual use in the U.S. was clearly less than the Paley study had expected.

In the case of tin, U.S. consumers deliberately sought alternative materials because of a perception that tin prices were high. The largest single use, tinplate, was substantially reduced by developing better coating methods that in effect made each pound of tin cover a larger area of steel. Furthermore tinplate itself lost markets to alternative materials in the packaging industry — aluminium, plastics, and glass. Solder, the second largest use, also lost ground to substitute materials, particularly in the automobile industry. Of all the major metals, over the third quarter of the century, tin showed the lowest rate of growth worldwide and its consumption in the United States declined.

Lead consumption grew at a slower rate than expected in the United States because of reduced demand for cable covering, for pigments, and for gasoline additives. The first of these was a technological development — the substitution of plastic-steel-aluminium composites for the lead sheathing that had traditionally been used both for power transmission and telecommunications cable. The loss of markets in pigments and in gasoline additives was heavily influenced by environmental concerns over the toxic properties of lead.

In the case of three other metals — copper, nickel and zinc — United States' consumption in 1973 was very close to the Paley estimates. One is inclined to give the Commission high marks for correctly estimating what would happen. Only in aluminium was 1973 consumption in the United States far in excess of the Paley forecast for 1975 (actually 89% higher).

By contrast, in the rest of the market-economy world the 1973 consumption of all nine materials, without exception, exceeded the Paley forecasts by a substantial margin. For tin and lead the percentages by which 1973 consumption in the rest of the world exceeded the Paley estimates for 1975 were 41% and 52% respectively.

In every other case, 1973 use outside the United States was at least double what the study had anticipated. The large gains made in iron ore, chromite and manganese consumption in the rest of the world were, of course, partly due to a factor already mentioned: United States internal needs for these commodities were met to a considerable degree by imports of steel-containing finished products, steel or ferro-alloys rather than by importing the raw materials or producing them at home.

Some Basic Factors Affecting Demand for Non-Fuel Minerals

The Paley Commission had concluded that consumption of almost all materials "is expanding at compound rates." Yet its forecasts proved to be too conservative — with the margin of error primarily outside the United States.

Growth in consumption does not occur in a smooth curve, however. For example, on a compound basis over the years 1950-73 the global consumption of aluminium increased 8% annually and the global consumption of copper increased 4% annually. In some years gains of as much as 30% over the consumption of the previous year were recorded for these metals. And in some years, despite the strong secular long-term uptrend in demand, consumption declined sharply. This was the case, for instance, in 1975, the Paley Commission target year.

Demand for raw materials is highly sensitive to the business cycle. Relatively modest fluctuations in the gross national product of a major mineral-consuming country can result in far wider swings in consumption of minerals.

Chart 2 illustrates this point. For the years 1973-77 it contrasts the annual changes in the gross national product of the United States, Japan, Germany F.R., and the United Kingdom with the consumption of copper and aluminium in each of those countries during those years.

The largest single gain in gross national product in any of the four countries was the gain of 9·6% registered in Japan in 1973 over 1972. The United Kingdom reported a 7·5% gain in gross national product, also in 1973. In the United States the largest year-to-year gain in gross national product was in 1976 over 1975, a rise of 5·7%. Germany F.R. had an identical gain for the same year.

Declines in gross national product are relatively infrequent and, when they occur, tend to be small. The largest loss shown during the five-year period covered by the tabulation was a decline of 2·5% in Germany F.R. in 1975, compared with 1974.

These changes in gross national product are stated on a 'deflated' basis. That is, the value of gross national product is measured in terms of currencies of constant value, to eliminate the influence of inflation.

19

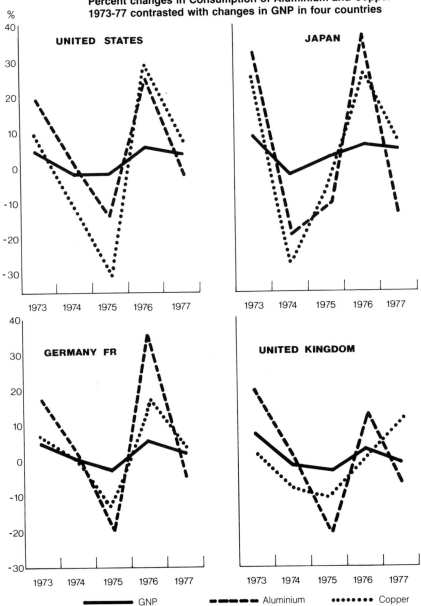

CHART 2. VOLATILITY OF MINERAL CONSUMPTION YEAR BY YEAR
Percent changes in Consumption of Aluminium and Copper
1973-77 contrasted with changes in GNP in four countries

UNITED STATES

JAPAN

GERMANY FR

UNITED KINGDOM

GNP ——— Aluminium ■—■—■ Copper ••••••••

Sources: GNP from Boston Consulting Group. Data deflated to constant
basis by calculations intended to eliminate influence of inflation.
Aluminium and Copper consumption percent changes based on
Metallgesellschaft yearbook.

The years 1973-77 inclusive were selected for the tabulation because this was a period of violent economic change. It therefore provides a valid litmus test to measure the influence of cycles on minerals consumption. The year 1973 had been the year of greatest economic activity yet recorded. The boom was brought to a sharp halt in mid-1974 by the dramatic energy crisis caused by steeply rising oil prices. This was followed by a severe recession in 1975. Fairly rapid recovery occurred in 1976 and 1977. These years, therefore, provide valid clues as to what happens to consumption of metals when sudden economic changes develop.

In contrast with the single-digit percentage changes in gross national product during these years in all four countries, at times consumption of aluminium and copper rose or fell by double-digit percentages in all four countries. Changes from year-to-year of as much as 30% occurred in the United States, Germany F.R. and Japan. In the United Kingdom the losses and gains were somewhat smaller but still far greater than the changes in the gross national product.

Thus, regardless of the long-term secular trends in consumption of minerals, an inescapable fact of life is that in the short term very pronounced changes will occur from year to year. This volatility arises from the large proportion of mineral consumption that is linked to industrial capital expenditures, construction activity, and on such major consumer durable items as automobiles, refrigerators, and other appliances.

Consumer expenditures on food, clothing, pharmaceuticals, cosmetics and other 'soft' items are less affected by economic conditions — use of such products cannot readily be deferred. But only a small share of mineral production goes into these areas — aluminium or tin-plated steel for food and beverage containers are one example. Even the use of agricultural minerals — phosphate, potash and sulphur — is affected by economic conditions as farmers tend to reduce purchases of fertilizers during downturns in the business cycle when farm-commodity prices are depressed.

In addition to the pronounced sensitivity of materials demand to the business cycle, a second major characteristic is that, with rare

21

exceptions, *over any extended period of time the consumption of raw materials grows more slowly than the economy as a whole.*

Technology is constantly finding ways to make more efficient use of materials. A few simple examples will illustrate:

Prior to World War II long-distance passenger travel, both national and international, was predominantly by rail or ocean liner. Today it is predominantly by air. A modern 747 aircraft, weighing about 200 tons, will carry more people between New York and Los Angeles in a week than a single passenger train weighing several thousand tons; in the same way a 747 aircraft will fly more people across the Atlantic in a week than would a 50,000-ton ocean liner.

The modern pocket calculator, weighing a few ounces, does its work more quickly and efficiently than a desk-top adding machine, weighing several pounds, did 30 years ago.

Telecommunications are being facilitated by optic fibres and by micro-wave relay stations, replacing copper cables between central switching points and carrying a far greater volume of messages.

Sometimes, of course, the development of technology requires large amounts of materials that in the past had small markets — and for these commodities gains in consumption may, at least temporarily, outstrip overall economic growth. Aluminium was a case in point during the third quarter of the century; the semi-conductor materials have enjoyed an extraordinary increase in demand; and consumption of platinum-group metals rose dramatically following the development of catalytic converters to deal with automotive exhaust gases. But these are the exceptions.

In the long run, the thrust of science is to use materials more efficiently — and this means that the quantities required will not increase as rapidly as the overall output of goods and services.

A third element in assessing long-term materials requirements, which may appear self-evident, is that sectors of the economy which are approaching market saturation offer fewer opportunities than sectors of the economy in which markets are relatively untapped. This simple truth appears to have been overlooked by those who made the Paley forecasts.

Translated into specific terms, consumption of materials in the United States during the years 1950-73 grew at a much lower rate than consumption of materials in the rest of the Free World because, by 1950, the United States market for automobiles and other consumer durables had already been well developed, whereas the market for these products in other countries was far from the saturation point. Moreover, manufacturers with modern industrial plants in other developed countries successfully penetrated the United States market in competition with U.S. manufacturers. This reduced U.S. needs for raw materials even though the ultimate end-user market for finished goods in the country continued to grow.

Minerals Demand and the Energy Crunch

Global consumption of minerals had undergone spectacular, if erratic, expansion in the years 1950-73 — far exceeding the Paley Commission's expectations. Over the next 12 years (1974-85) consumption grew at a far lower and more erratic pace. The drastic increase in oil prices in late 1973 and early 1974 had profoundly altered the world economy.

Soaring energy costs had fundamental effects on the Free World's industrial structure besides increasing the frequency and volatility of the business cycle. Until 1973 oil prices had been, if anything, weak in periods of inflation. The world had become accustomed to cheap and plentiful petroleum products. Then in the third quarter of 1973, the outbreak of renewed war in the Middle East caused the Arab nations to declare an embargo on oil shipments to countries trading with Israel. Spot shortages brought about rising prices. Early in 1974 the Organization of Petroleum Exporting Countries (OPEC) tripled its export price for crude oil overnight. Its control over oil moving in international trade, while far from complete, was sufficient to bring about a dramatic change in the market. The rise in oil prices caused:

Concern that cartels would be formed in many other industrial commodities.

Massive increases in foreign indebtedness by many oil-importing nations.

Currency instability arising from altered trade flows.

Almost panicky switching of investments by investors seeking to ensure maximum liquidity, with consequent reluctance to make long-term commitments.

Distortions in competitive cost positions within individual industries, depending on the degree of energy-intensity.

Alterations in the patterns of commodity consumption arising from efforts to economize on energy use.

The belief that cartels would be formed for most commodities involved in international trade was widespread in 1974 and 1975. At a special session of the United Nations, held in the spring of 1974, representatives of many commodity-exporting Third World Countries spoke at length on this theme. They argued that the terms of trade between the raw-material exporters and the importing manufacturers of industrial goods had been unfairly distorted in the past by buyers' markets in commodities. They predicted that producers' associations of other commodities would model themselves on OPEC and swing the balance of power to the sellers.

Among the mineral commodities which these speakers suggested might be cartelized were bauxite, copper, phosphate rock, mercury, tungsten and iron ore. But — except for the prototype, oil — it was not to be. Efforts made in bauxite and mercury proved ineffective. The copper exporters' association, CIPEC, had numerous discussions on the price situation but failed to agree on a plan for stability. The pervasive recession of 1975 proved that the law of supply and demand still ruled the market place for most minerals.

Higher oil prices hastened the search for alternative energy sources. The list was long — abundant coal, natural gas, oil shale, uranium, undeveloped hydro-power, geothermal steam, ocean tides, solar energy, timber, even windmills. Efforts were made in each direction. But the capital and/or operating costs of developing new supplies or of converting old facilities were high. At first only marginal incursions were made into the demand for oil.

Thus, for six years OPEC appeared invincible. Prices of oil rose steadily, culminating in a final upward thrust in 1979, a year when the public feared an actual oil shortage. But after 1979 the balance swung slowly the other way. Added oil production by non-OPEC countries, combined with a levelling off in oil demand, brought rising inventories and eventually weakened prices. Strains arose within OPEC as some members marketed quantities in excess of agreed quotas. The protracted war between two leading OPEC members — Iran and Iraq — caused them to produce less than their quotas but it failed to restore strength to the market.

After 10 years, OPEC no longer appeared invincible. In 1974 it had seemed that the oil crisis was the first manifestation of the "larger and more pervasive" materials problem which the Paley Commission had cited in 1950. But by 1984 higher prices had clearly brought supply and demand back into balance. Moreover, the anticipated exhaustion of oil reserves (which in 1974 had been generally perceived as occurring in the first quarter of the next century at the latest) seemed far less imminent — thanks both to new discoveries and to a lower than anticipated level of demand. Oil's share of total energy supply in the United States had been 46·7% in 1973. By 1984 it had fallen to 42%. Inevitably it will fall further.

The rise in oil prices had placed a special burden on oil-importing countries, particularly many developing countries. They had to pay for oil imports in hard currency. The recession induced by higher oil prices cut into the demand for and reduced the prices of their exports. Thus, these nations were faced with a substantial deterioration in hard currency earnings and, in consequence, in their ability to pay for oil imports. Their only recourse was to borrow in the international capital markets. The size of their foreign debts mounted swiftly.

At the same time, interest rates rose sharply — spurred not only by increased demand from borrowers but also by increasing inflation. Interest rates typically are at a premium over inflation rates, otherwise lenders would not earn a 'real' return on their loans. Higher interest rates compound the problems of all borrowers — individuals, private business enterprises and governments.

The changed flows of international trade destabilized exchange rates for the major world currencies. Following the U.S. action in 1971 in terminating the link between gold and the dollar at $35 an ounce, currency exchange rates had been allowed to float. After the oil price rise, fluctuations became increasingly pronounced among the major international currencies — the dollar, the pound sterling, the yen, the deutschmark, and the Swiss franc. The values of the currencies of the developing countries fell sharply.

Instability made investors uneasy. Increasingly they chose to turn away from long-term commitments in an effort to achieve maximum liquidity. During the decade 1974-83 they scrambled wildly and frequently into and out of various types of investment — precious metals, collectables such as works of art and antiques, stocks, bonds, money market funds, foreign exchange, commodities.

But investors were wary of long-term capital-intensive major projects for expansion of industrial capacity. One exception was major industrialization projects in the oil-exporting countries, the early gainers in the race for hard currency. Numerous steel, aluminium and petro-chemical plants were built in these countries during the late seventies. Several turned out to be white elephants because they lacked soundly planned infrastructure, had limited domestic markets and were short of adequate skilled labour.

Elsewhere, new large scale projects were faced with heavy capital costs that put them at a severe disadvantage compared with facilities built during the 60s and early 70s at lower interest rates and lower capital costs. A full discussion as it applies to mineral projects will be found in Chapter 3.

Higher oil prices and consequent higher costs for all forms of energy (except, perhaps, for hydro-electric power already in place) had serious spin-off effects on competition within existing industries.

A relevant example is the experience of the nickel industry. The sharp rise in the demand for nickel during the 1950-73 period (6% compounded annually) had encouraged rapid growth in nickel-producing capacity. Once largely concentrated in the sulphide nickel-copper deposits of Canada, over the 1950-73 period new nickel mines had been developed in other countries — Indonesia, New Caledonia, the Philippines, Australia, the Dominican Republic, Guatemala and elsewhere. Most of these new projects involved the extraction of nickel from lateritic ores, requiring extensive inputs of fuel. For the most part these plants were oil-based. With the dramatic leap in oil costs, their competitive position was drastically undermined in relation to the sulphide mines. The lag in capital spending cut severely into the demand for nickel. Inventories mounted and the price of nickel sagged. By 1981-82 many of these new projects were operating at substantial losses.

Perhaps the most lasting influence of higher oil prices has been to redouble efforts to reduce energy consumption. An obvious and early target was energy used in transportation — particularly in automotive vehicles. To increase the mileage obtained per unit of fuel consumed, the automotive industry embarked on a campaign to increase the efficiency of the engines and to reduce the weight of the vehicles. As a consequence, every component was analyzed. Substitutions were sought for steel (to the advantage of aluminium) and where substitutions were impractical, steel of greater strength but lighter weight was used. Plastic mouldings were substituted for zinc die castings. Lead batteries were made lighter and more efficient.

The sum total of these various spin-offs arising from the oil price increases was that the sharply ascending curve of minerals consumption prior to 1973 was replaced by a trend line that in the years after 1974 became nearly horizontal. Still highly sensitive to the influence of the business cycle, mineral consumption nevertheless continued to trend modestly upward.

This is illustrated by Chart 3 which presents the data for annual consumption of six metals over the entire period 1950-85. Prior to the OPEC action on oil prices, for most minerals peak consumption had been attained in 1973 or 1974. After the sharp recession of 1975, consumption rose to new record levels for most minerals by 1978 or 1979. In 1980-82 a fresh recession set in, the consequence of the oil price rises of 1979. But although mineral consumption fell, it did not drop as low as in 1975. Thus, on the up side, consumption in 1979 exceeded consumption in 1973, tin and zinc excepted. On the down side, consumption in 1982 did not fall as low as consumption in 1975, tin again excepted.

On the whole, therefore, the conclusion seems warranted that world mineral consumption is still growing — but at a pace far more modest than that which prevailed prior to 1974.

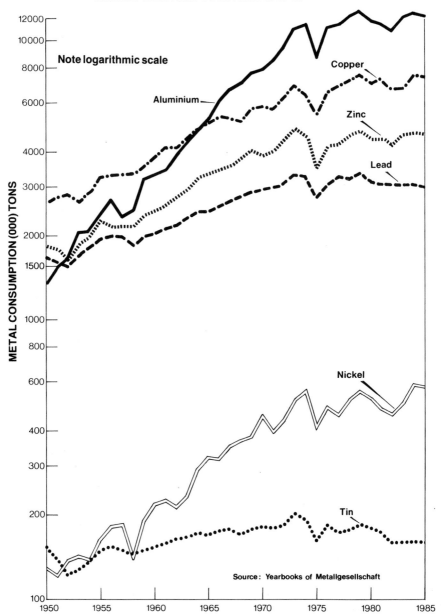

CHART   3.   METAL CONSUMPTION IN
             MARKET-ECONOMY COUNTRIES 1950-85

Note logarithmic scale

Aluminium

Copper

Zinc

Lead

Nickel

Tin

METAL CONSUMPTION (000) TONS

Source: Yearbooks of Metallgesellschaft

28

Assessing the Future of Minerals Consumption

What will be the pattern of consumption of minerals in the future? Will it revert to the extraordinary growth rates experienced in the 1950-73 period? Is the much slower pace of expansion that has occurred since 1974 more representative of what the future will bring? Is it likely that growth will cease entirely and an actual shrinkage in the use of minerals might occur?

"Prophecy is the most gratuitous form of error" wrote George Eliot. Experience with forecasts in the minerals field appears to bear her out. Nevertheless, in any form of economic activity — and certainly in planning new undertakings in mineral production and consumption — an assessment of probable future trends is essential.

Since mid-century mineral consumption trends have been largely shaped by at least four significant broad-based forces (macro-economic factors in the language of professional economists). What role will they play in the future?

The first of these forces has been the unremitting growth in world population. Although birth rates in many countries are now declining, advances in health care have increased life expectancy. Demographers agree that for many years to come population gains will continue. That means the number of customers requiring mineral raw materials will continue to rise.

The second force has been the rapid advance of science and technology. Scientific research undertaken by academic institutions, governments and private industry has created a bewildering array of new industries and new products which require greater varieties and more sophisticated qualities of raw materials. That this trend will continue can be regarded as certain.

Less assurance can be felt about the two remaining major forces. The third has been cited previously — the post-war restoration of the industrial infrastructure of Western Europe and Japan, followed by the rapid increase in the standard of living of their inhabitants. These nations have now reached a stage of industrial development that suggests further growth will be at a slower pace — approximating the more gradual rise experienced in the United States between 1950 and 1974.

29

If this is so, will another group of countries emerge and will their industrialization provide a comparable stimulus to global mineral consumption? Until a few years ago there was a general expectation that the stimulus would come from industrialization of several populous developing countries.

Then, however, the onset of the energy crisis and the turmoil that ensued became the fourth major macro-economic factor to influence mineral consumption. Unlike the other forces mentioned, its influence proved adverse.

Beginning in 1974 the economic scene underwent wrenching change. Patterns of international trade were greatly altered, exchange rates for all currencies became unstable, interest rates soared, inflation raged in virtually every country, and many developing nations faced overwhelming debt burdens arising from trade imbalances. Painful readjustments were forced on the world economy. Two periods of severe world recession after 1974 cut mineral consumption sharply. For most minerals market growth over the 12-year span to 1985 was slight.

Just as the Paley Commission had underestimated the enormous stimulus to mineral demand arising from the rehabilitation of the war-shattered industries of Western Europe and Japan, so few observers had correctly foreseen the fateful consequences of the prolonged energy crisis.

Looking ahead, there may be similar unforeseen and unpredictable events that will have dramatic impact on the world's economic health over the balance of the century. Perhaps the drastic drop in oil prices in 1985-86 may bring about a period of reduced inflation, low interest rates, and improved trade balances for many countries. If so, perhaps a solid basis for renewed economic expansion may be laid. Low inflation suggests that raw material prices are unlikely to display much buoyancy and that raw material producers will have to reduce production costs to achieve satisfactory financial outcomes.

Barring some entirely unexpected development, the greatest potential for further growth in mineral consumption appears to lie in an improvement of living standards in the developing nations. Is it possible to create new markets among those countries that will parallel what occurred during the third quarter of the century in Western Europe and Japan?

In percentage terms, mineral consumption in some developing countries had made sharp gains during the third quarter of the century. But as these gains were made from extremely low bases, aggregate quantities of minerals consumed in the developing world represented only a small share of the global market.

Calculated on a *per capita* basis consumption of minerals in developing countries is perhaps one-tenth of what it is in the developed countries. For some purposes, *per capita* consumption figures have their limitations. They represent the amount of raw material used within a country. If a country imports manufactured products, the mineral components of those imports have been calculated in the *per capita* consumption of the manufacturing country rather than the country where the product is actually being used. Thus, considering the heavy trade in manufactured products among developed countries, *per capita* consumption data on minerals may not be fully representative. However, the developing countries are relatively small importers of manufactured products and so their consumption data can be taken as roughly correct.

The drive to industrialize was widely accepted political strategy for many developing countries before the energy crisis broke. In the early 70s, Brazil was being spoken of as the 'next Japan'.

Mexico, the Republic of Korea, Iran, Taiwan, and Venezuela had ambitious programmes for modernization. The countries of the Arabian peninsula were pressing forward with schemes to use their abundant supplies of oil and gas.

That the people of the developing world would welcome an improvement in their living standards is obvious. And if these aspirations can be realized they will inevitably involve a much larger call on the world's material resources. But as the past few years have shown, achieving the goals of industrialization will be difficult for these nations. The problems have been exacerbated by the wrenching effects of higher oil prices.

In the years since 1977 a debt crisis has materially altered the economic plans of the countries of Latin America and Africa. Having

31

borrowed heavily through loans with floating interest rates to finance their ambitious plans, the combination of soaring interest rates and depressed commodity prices has caused a debt crisis. To avoid default maturity dates have been re-negotiated but austerity measures have been imposed which dampen economic growth in the debtor nations.

The countries of Africa, South Africa excepted, have had little success in achieving industrialization. Many of them have faced massive difficulties arising from periods of intense drought at a time when their populations have been increasing rapidly.

In the specific case of Iran, under the Shah an effort was being made to create a modern industrial state. Following the revolution that brought Ayatollah Khomeini to power, the country has altered course. Whether Iran still desires to industrialize is a moot point and, even if the desire is present, whether it can be achieved appears questionable.

In much of Asia, where the Japanese model has been emulated, visible progress has resulted from focusing industrial efforts on labour-intensive projects rather than on the massive capital-intensive undertakings that have been launched by other developing areas.

Taken as a group, the countries of the Third World do not now appear to be on the brink of the kind of economic growth achieved by the industrialized countries in the post-war era. Struggling with massive debts, lack of sources of internal capital, political unrest, low living and educational standards, and burgeoning populations, the developing nations will do well to achieve modest economic gains in the years ahead.

Thus, most observers currently would be inclined to forecast gains in minerals demand at rates lower than those projected prior to 1975. Still, given the demographic curves expected for world population over the next three or four decades and continued scientific advances, on balance the consensus is that consumption of minerals will continue to rise (although this may not necessarily apply to every major mineral product).

Will increased demand cause such a drain on the earth's resources during that period as to bring about the "larger and more pervasive" problems feared by the Paley Commission?

CHAPTER TWO

Availability of Minerals

Measuring Reserves

Nagging fears of mineral shortages have been a recurring theme —
almost an obsession — since the dawn of the industrial age focused
public attention on the essential role minerals play in the world's
economy.

These concerns are understandable. Supplies of animal and
vegetable products are replenished through the process of reproduc-
tion. Minerals do not reproduce. They are non-renewable resources.
Their use in many instances can be extended through recycling of
salvaged scrap, but the only new source of minerals for mankind's
needs lies in what is dug out of the earth or raised from under the sea.

Because most mineral resources are hidden deep within the globe,
measurement of their extent is difficult. No one can know with
certainty how great these resources are. As consumption rises, the
suspicion intensifies that complete exhaustion is imminent. The Paley
Commission's deep misgivings, expressed in its omnibus study
published in 1951, have already been cited.

An even gloomier assessment was made 22 years earlier. In an
article published in 1929, *St. Nicholas Magazine* (a United States
publication catering for children between the ages of six and fifteen)
warned that available deposits of oil, copper, lead and zinc would be
exhausted by 1950. Thus, by the time its readers had children of their
own they would have to adjust to a much lower standard of living.

This sombre conclusion was based on a misunderstanding of a
study by the U.S. Bureau of Mines. The Bureau had published
estimates in 1929 that known reserves of many principal minerals

were equal to between 15 and 20 years at then current rates of consumption. These estimates were based on conservative engineering principles, well understood by professionals but not familiar to the lay public.

In estimating potential supplies of minerals, geologists and mining engineers refer both to reserves and to resources. By reserves they mean measured quantities contained in deposits that are currently economically viable. These deposits have been sufficiently well identified by drilling or other means of exploration to establish with reasonable certainty the quantities and the quality of the minerals contained within the area explored. However, once what appears to be a viable deposit has been defined, further costly exploration is often discontinued to conserve capital. After operations begin, exploration may be resumed in tandem with production. Thus, reserves at any given time rarely exceed the immediately foreseeable requirement of the enterprise.

In contrast with reserves, mining engineers and geologists classify resources as those deposits that either do not appear to be economically viable under current conditions or that have been insufficiently explored to ascertain with reasonable certainty the quantity or the quality of the minerals contained. With time, as market conditions change, as new technology develops or as additional exploration is undertaken, deposits once considered to constitute resources may be reclassified as reserves.

When a scientific organization estimates that, say, known reserves of copper ores will meet global requirements for 20 years at present consumption rates, this should not be interpreted to mean (as *St. Nicholas Magazine* did) that in 20 years copper will cease to be available. What is meant is only that a 20-year reserve has been carefully assessed, with as yet unmeasured potential for additional supplies. Unfortunately, the reporting by the media frequently conveys less than a correct explanation. The public, scanning such reports hastily, derives a mistaken and overly pessimistic impression.

Furthermore, beyond known reserves and resources of minerals, there also exists the shadowy potential of geologically promising areas in which exploration has been insufficient to determine either

34

the extent or the quality of mineral deposits. Alaska in the United States, the newly independent country of Papua New Guinea, and much of Brazil are examples of vast areas in which studies of the mineral potential have barely begun — and yet the work done has already identified great mineral riches.

Crustal Abundance

The elements contained in the earth's surface are numerous and their quantities vary enormously. These variations have important implications for the structure of the individual mineral industries. The three metals most widely used today are iron, aluminium and copper. The first two are plentiful but copper is relatively scarce.

Calculations have been made of the percentage of each element contained in the earth's crust. Like estimates of reserves and resources, these estimates must be considered as imprecise, but they do give a useful impression of the order of magnitude. Table 2 represents the quantities estimated by B. J. Skinner in his book *Earth Resources*.

TABLE 2: CHEMICAL ELEMENTS AND THEIR CRUSTAL ABUNDANCES

Name	Crustal Abundance, Weight %	Name	Crustal Abundance, Weight %
Aluminium	8·00	Mercury	0·000002
Antimony	0·00002	Molybdenum	0·00012
Arsenic	0·00020	Nickel	0·0072
Bismuth	0·0000004	Nitrogen	0·0020
Cadmium	0·000018	Oxygen	45·2
Carbon	0·02	Phosphorus	0·1010
Chromium	0·0096	Platinum	0·0000005
Cobalt	0·0028	Potassium	1·68
Copper	0·0058	Selenium	0·000005
Fluorine	0·0460	Silicon	27·20
Gold	0·0000002	Silver	0·000008
Iodine	0·00005	Sulphur	0·030
Iron	5·80	Tellurium	0·000001
Lead	0·0010	Tin	0·00015
Lithium	0·0020	Titanium	0·86
Magnesium	2·77	Zinc	0·0082
Manganese	0·100		

Source: *Earth Resources*, by B. J. Skinner

Oxygen and silicon together account for over 70% of all the elements in the earth's crust. Next in order are aluminium (8%) and iron (5·8%), the basic source of steel.

Within the market-economy countries, substantially all aluminium production is derived from bauxite (although work has been and is being done on other minerals such as alunite, nepheline, and various clays). With an aluminium content of over 25%, only four tons of high-grade bauxite are required for a ton of metal.

In the case of iron and steel, even higher-grade ores are available. The two minerals most commonly mined to produce pig iron are magnetite (iron content 72·4%) and hematite (69·4%). The high-grade deposits being mined in Australia and Brazil are relatively free of dilution by other minerals. Lower-grade ores are being mined elsewhere — notably in the United States and Europe — which require some concentration prior to conversion into pig iron. On average, however, the pig-iron industry processes less than two tons of ore to produce a ton of pig iron.

By contrast, the copper industry is treating low-grade ores. Copper represents only 0·0058% of the earth's crust, according to Skinner — in other words, 58 parts per million. There has been some production of native copper (metal existing in its pure state in nature) and in the past relatively high-grade ores have been found in small deposits. Currently most of the world's production comes from ores containing 1% copper or less. In the United States the typical copper mine in recent years has extracted 200 tons of ore to produce a ton of metal.

To maintain copper production, therefore, the industry must discover 200 tons of new reserves for each ton of metal produced; whereas the aluminium industry needs to find only four tons of reserves and the steel industry only two tons of reserves.

The costs of finding and mining ore are the chief elements in the economics of copper; the costs of transporting and processing ore are the chief elements in the economics of aluminium and steel. The three metals compete with each other but to a major extent they march to different drummers.

Lead, nickel, tin and zinc — like copper — are other base metal industries in which the finding and mining of ore deposits are crucial to the economic success of an enterprise. Even more discovery-sensitive are the precious metals — gold, silver, and the platinum metals. The search for them is akin to the proverbial hunt for the needle in a haystack. The greatest gold field in the world's history has been the Witwatersrand in South Africa. On average, to produce one ton of gold, the Witwatersrand mines handle 150,000 tons of ore. In other parts of the world ores of still lower grade are being mined and processed. For example, some of the newer mines in the United States are producing gold from ores with a content of one gramme per ton, so that one million tons of ore are processed to yield one ton of gold.

The Bingham Pit: A Classic Example of Expanding Reserves

To illustrate how mineral reserves may be initially greatly under-stated, consider the history of the Bingham pit. This copper mine in Utah, currently operated by Kennecott Copper, first came to public attention at the turn of the century. In 1900 an enterprising young mining engineer, D. C. Jackling, sought to raise a few million dollars to equip the deposit for copper production by open-pit methods.

His prospectus (which naturally strove to put the best possible face on the project) stated that the deposit contained reserves of 12 million tons of copper ore with an average content of 2% copper or 240,000 tons of copper content. By the standards prevailing in those days, a 2% content was considered extremely low-grade copper ore. Initially the enterprise was derisively known as Jackling's folly. All U.S. copper mines then being exploited had ore of higher copper content and were being worked by underground methods.

By 1906 Jackling had raised the funds he needed, built the necessary plant, and begun production. The mine operated almost continuously until 1985, when it closed temporarily due to adverse economic conditions — not due to exhaustion of resources. In almost 80 years it had produced over 13 million tons of copper from 1,700 million tons of ore — plus large quantities of by-product molybdenum, gold and silver. Thus, Jackling's original estimate amounted to less than 1% of the ore and 2% of the copper already produced.

In late 1985 Standard Oil, which now owns Kennecott Copper and thus the Bingham pit, announced plans to invest $400 million to modernize the facilities with the intention of resuming production no later than 1988 at a capacity of 185,000 tons of copper a year. This annual capacity is more than three-quarters of the original estimate of the mine's entire copper content.

Mr. Jackling had not sought to deceive the public as to the size or potential of the deposit. As a professional engineer, he claimed as reserves only that quantity of ore already defined that he felt could be profitably mined with the technology and at the copper prices then prevailing.

In the years since the operation began, technological advance and economies of scale have made it possible to mine lower grades of ore (currently the average quality of ore being mined is about 0·6% copper). As production has progressed, exploration has greatly expanded the boundaries of the deposit beyond what was known to Mr. Jackling. With the limited capital available he could not have drilled out the entire deposit — nor indeed would it have been wise to attempt to do so, given the size of the 1900 copper market.

The specific example of the Bingham mine is not unique. Significant strides in the mining and processing of minerals have been made during the twentieth century that have greatly extended the parameters within which productive mineral operations can take place. Due to the development of more efficient and productive equipment, costs have been well contained. As a consequence, prices of most minerals have not risen in relation to the prices of other goods.

Those who seek to arrive at conclusions about the adequacy of mineral supplies to meet future demand need to recognize the limitations surrounding estimates of reserves and resources. Supplies of minerals are indeed finite. But knowledge about the extent of these finite supplies is far from complete.

Why The Paley Commission Underestimated Available Supplies
In judging the availability of future mineral supplies, the Paley Commission took a sombre view. It expressed concern that "larger

and more pervasive" problems would develop. It doubted that adequate amounts would be furnished to meet its consumption forecasts which themselves proved too conservative. The difficulties should, in fact, have been horrendous by now.

Relatively few significant additions had been made to world mineral supplies in the two decades before the Paley report was written. Undoubtedly this influenced the Commission to believe that most mineral resources had already been discovered and relatively few remained to be found.

Discoveries had been minimal during those 20 years because exploration efforts had been curtailed. The great Depression of the Thirties had driven prices for most minerals to extremely low levels as demand dropped and available capacity was under-utilized. Mining companies struggled to remain solvent. Their expenditures on exploration were cut to the bone.

Then World War II broke out. Production of minerals was accelerated but available manpower was reduced by the drafting of able-bodied men into the armed services. Many promising mineral-bearing areas were involved in military operations. It was no time to hunt for new deposits, except perhaps for some small-tonnage militarily-significant materials.

So, if for 20 years new finds were few, the reason was that the searches had been few.

This situation changed dramatically with the return to peace. As mineral consumption rose and higher prices provided incentives, mining companies sent out exploration teams to look for new resources. They succeeded to an extent few had envisaged — certainly not the Paley Commission.

The Paley study had assessed potential supplies on a commodity-by-commodity basis. Its forecasts of resource availability proved even wider of the mark than its conclusions as to growth in demand.

During the period 1950-75 covered by the Commission forecasts, discoveries of new deposits and extensions of previously known occurrences added far more to identified global mineral reserves of every commodity than had been consumed during those 25 years. By the mid-seventies, abundance rather than scarcity was the prevalent

39

condition among the non-fuel minerals. This is still the case today.

Mineral exploration in the post-war years proved astonishingly successful in identifying huge reserves and/or resources in areas not previously involved in production of specific materials. Those who in 1950 foresaw early limitations to economic development because of depletion of non-renewable resources failed to appreciate how much of the earth's surface remained to be explored.

The Australian Experience

The island continent of Australia provides an outstanding example of mineral discovery during this period.

Australia had long been a focus for mineral exploration. First settled early in the nineteenth century, the discovery of gold in mid-century brought to its shores experienced miners from every corner of the globe. They tramped the vast continent which — unlike land areas with heavy vegetation — offered enormous expanses of arid land with clearly visible geological features. They found gold, silver, lead, zinc, tin, and some copper before the outbreak of World War II.

But, as of 1950, Australia had little or no production of bauxite (the ore of aluminium), nickel, manganese or diamonds. Its known iron-ore reserves were limited. To conserve these for its own burgeoning steel industry, the government embargoed iron-ore exports. Australia's copper production was about equal to its modest home consumption.

In its discussion of resources of iron ore, bauxite, nickel, manganese, copper and industrial diamonds, the Paley Commission report had made no reference to Australia as a potential contributor to world supplies.

Yet today Australia is by a substantial margin the world's largest bauxite producer. It ranks with Brazil as one of the two largest producers and exporters of iron ore in the market-economy world. It is also the second largest nickel producer. Among market-economy manganese-mining countries it ranks fifth. Its annual copper production has expanded tenfold since the Paley study was published. If a huge and as yet untapped deposit in South Australia is brought into production, as planned, Australian copper production could double again in the 1990s.

As for diamonds, only a few years ago discoveries of major resources were made in Western Australia. Production began in 1983 and is expected to attain a scale by the end of the decade that will make Australia the world's largest producer in terms of quantity. Because the bulk of the output is of industrial quality diamonds, however, the value of output will be less than that of South Africa.

The Australian developments vividly illustrate what sweeping changes can occur in world supply prospects for a specific commodity as a result of exploration of areas that are geologically promising.

But the Australian experience is not unique. In every continent, major mineral discoveries have been made since 1950. This has been the result not only of redoubled efforts but also of advances in prospecting techniques and geological science. Significant new resources have been identified in countries not previously important as sources of minerals. They also have been found in developed countries which have long histories of mining activity.

Take the case of the United States. Based on advice of United States' Government scientists in 1950, the Paley Commission made gloomy assessments of future prospects for two U.S. mature mining industries — copper and lead.

The Paley Report cited United States' copper reserve estimates of 22·5 million tons of contained metal. It concluded that "a long-run domestic mine production capacity of 800,000 short tons (720,000 metric tons) a year seems the best that can safely be assured." It asserted that "the copper industry appears already to have exploited fairly exhaustively the possibilities provided by advances in technology to date . . . the chance of further discovery outside the known districts is small."

In 1980 the U.S. Geological Survey estimated the U.S. copper reserves as 91·6 million tons, four times the estimate contained in the Paley Report 30 years earlier — despite production in the interim of about 37 million tons. Production in the single year of 1973 exceeded 1·55 million tons — more than double the Paley estimated maximum.

41

Of the 25 largest U.S. copper-producing mines in 1981, 16 had begun production since 1950. Ten of these were in districts which had no production in 1950.

The lead mining industry of the United States also confounded the Paley experts. In 1950 United States mine production was 390,000 tons of lead. The Paley Report concluded that "the best that can be hoped for is that domestic mine production will not decline by more than 50% by 1975". In other words, to 200,000 tons a year or less. Another comment was that "the poor discovery record of the past few decades provides little basis for optimism that the equivalent of the southeast Missouri district can be expected to turn up in the future".

In 1974 United States mines produced in excess of 600,000 tons. Since 1970, the country has been the Free World's largest lead miner except for the occasional year in which labour difficulties have arisen. Lead mine production has been more than twice as great as the Paley expectation.

The great bulk of this output comes from central Missouri in the district known as the Viburnum Trend. Exploration uncovered massive deposits there in the late 1950s and early 1960s. Ironically, the area is only a few score miles from the old southeast Missouri district to which the Paley Report referred and which has now been largely depleted — although a sustained period of high prices and good demand for lead might well cause a revival of exploration there, as often occurs with old mining areas.

Two other industrialized countries that have experienced comparable expansion of mineral reserves and added productive capacity of large dimensions since the publication of the Paley Report are Canada and South Africa.

Canadian mine production of nickel has expanded only modestly since 1950 as other countries have become significant producers and captured part of the market that in the early 1950s was dominated by Canada. However, one major new nickel district has been developed in Manitoba, testifying to the amplitude of Canadian resources. Among the other base metals, Canadian mine output has quadrupled in zinc, tripled in copper, and doubled in lead.

Much of the new lead and zinc production has come from the Northwest Territory, the Yukon, and the islands of the Arctic Ocean, where Canadian engineering skill has overcome the difficulties of adverse climate and enormous distances to demonstrate that the resources of these remote regions can be made available to mankind.

Of the added copper production in Canada, a large share derives from numerous low-grade deposits in British Columbia. These have an important by-product output of molybdenum. No mention of Canada as a potential source was made in the brief Paley discussion of molybdenum which expressed the opinion that "of total future supply only about one-fifth may be produced outside the United States". This, too, was an erroneous conclusion. In recent years about 40% of market-economy molybdenum production has come from outside the United States. Canada and Chile each have produced between 12% and 15% of the global molybdenum supply since the late 1970s.

In the case of South Africa, huge increases have occurred in its mineral production since 1950: production of chrome ore is up sixfold; copper and manganese production is seven times as great as it was then; iron ore output has multiplied by 15 times; and, most remarkable of all, the yield of platinum metals is 20 times greater.

South Africa and the Soviet Union together account for over 90% of global platinum metals production, as well as three-fifths of world output of manganese and chrome ores.

Curiously, the Paley Report did not deal with precious metals — gold, silver, and the platinum metals. Although industrial use of gold is relatively limited, silver and the platinum metals have highly significant applications in industry, including many in the defence field. Thus, adequacy of future precious metal supply has an important bearing on world economic activity. Although South Africa is only a modest supplier of silver, its enormous reserves of platinum metals constitute the chief source for the market-economy countries, despite minor occurrences in Canada, Colombia and elsewhere.

Additional mineral resources of comparable magnitude have also been identified in developing countries during the years since the Paley study was completed. Some discoveries have been made in countries long known for their mining industries, countries such as Mexico, Chile and Peru. Other finds have been made and developed in nations such as Brazil, Indonesia and the Philippines, formerly regarded primarily as producers of agricultural commodities. And some highly significant additions have resulted from exploration in countries such as Papua New Guinea, Gabon, and Guinea which, 50 years ago, were largely outside the mainstream of world commerce.

The Changing Geography of Mineral Production

Not only have production volumes of many minerals risen dramatically, but massive shifts have taken place in the geographical distribution of production. To illustrate these trends, 10 of the major bulk minerals have been briefly analyzed, contrasting output among market-economy nations in 1950 with output in 1985. The data are based on the reports of the U.S. Bureau of Mines (the 1985 figures being subject to minor revision). The four largest individual producing nations in each of the two years are identified as well as their share of the global totals for the market-economy countries.

BAUXITE

Thanks to the extraordinary growth in aluminium consumption between 1950 and 1985, bauxite production increased 825%. The four countries that were the leading producers in 1950 are still producing bauxite today but they are no longer among the leaders in 1985. This provides a dramatic illustration of how market forces have stimulated exploration and resulted in discoveries in new areas. Of the four new leading bauxite producers, only Brazil was a bauxite miner in 1950 and its output was minuscule.

Bauxite ('000 t) in 1950			Bauxite ('000 t) in 1985		
Country	Output	% of Total	Country	Output	% of Total
Surinam	2,081	29	Australia	27,000	41
Guyana	1,609	22	Guinea	12,000	18
United States	1,356	19	Brazil	6,000	9
France	805	11	Jamaica	5,300	8
All others	1,349	19	All others	16,300	24
Aggregate	7,200		Aggregate	66,600	

44

CHROME ORE

Although the aggregate output of chrome ore has increased 235%, South Africa's enormous reserves have enabled that country to increase its market share significantly. The two next largest producers, Turkey and Zimbabwe, have increased production during the 35-year interval but their share of the market total has fallen sharply. Chrome ore is exceptional in that production in countries other than the four leaders was proportionately less in 1985 than in 1950.

Chrome Ore ('000 t) in 1950			**Chrome Ore ('000 t) in 1985**		
Country	Output	% of Total	Country	Output	% of Total
South Africa	496	29	South Africa	3,300	58
Turkey	421	25	Turkey	700	12
Zimbabwe	292	17	Zimbabwe	500	9
Philippines	251	15	India	500	9
All others	240	14	All others	700	12
Aggregate	1,700		Aggregate	5,700	

COPPER

Despite an increase in production of 27% between 1950 and 1985, the United States' copper mining industry's share of the market-economy output dropped from 36% to 16% during the period. The new leader, Chile, has huge reserves of good quality ore and also has efficient low costs. Zambian production is higher than it was at mid-century but it accounts for a sharply reduced share of the total and the country is no longer one of the four leaders. Meanwhile, the share of the aggregate output coming from the 'other countries' category has risen sharply. Among the major new sources of copper are Peru, the Philippines, Australia, South Africa, Mexico, and Papua New Guinea — all countries which in 1950 had little or no copper mining activity.

Copper ('000 t) in 1950			**Copper ('000 t) in 1985**		
Country	Output	% of Total	Country	Output	% of Total
United States	825	36	Chile	1,290	20
Chile	363	16	United States	1,050	16
Zambia	259	11	Canada	710	11
Canada	239	11	Zaire	540	8
All others	584	26	All others	2,800	44
Aggregate	2,270		Aggregate	6,390	

IRON ORE

Prior to 1950 international trade in iron ore was fairly limited. This was due to the existence of iron ore deposits in virtually every country and also to the high cost of transport in relation to the commodity's low value. This has changed. Development of mammoth bulk-cargo ore carriers, the discovery of extensive, extremely high-grade deposits in Australia, Brazil and other countries, and the sharp expansion of steel production at or close to deep-water ports have resulted in a great stimulus to international iron-ore transactions. In 1950 the four principal iron-ore producing countries were in major steel centres. In 1985 the two largest miners are chiefly iron-ore exporters.

Iron Ore ('000 t) in 1950			Iron Ore ('000t) in 1985		
Country	Output	% of Total	Country	Output	% of Total
United States	99,619	47	Brazil	95,000	22
France	29,983	14	Australia	90,000	20
Sweden	13,927	7	United States	48,000	10
Germany (F.R.)	10,882	5	India	42,000	8
All others	56,590	27	All others	184,000	40
Aggregate	211,000		Aggregate	459,000	

LEAD

Lead is the only one of the 10 minerals summarized to have shown an expansion in mineral production of less than 100% over the 35 years. Lead has also exhibited less change in the pattern of production distribution than the others. In 1985 Australia exceeded the United States in the volume of lead mine production but, in most recent years, the U.S. has been the leader among the market-economy countries. Peru has replaced Mexico in the 'first-four' grouping, but Mexico continues to be a substantial producer.

Lead ('000 t) in 1950			Lead ('000 t) in 1985		
Country	Output	% of Total	Country	Output	% of Total
United States	391	26	Australia	480	19
Mexico	238	16	United States	400	16
Australia	223	15	Canada	280	11
Canada	150	10	Peru	200	8
All others	506	34	All others	1,120	45
Aggregate	1,508		Aggregate	2,480	

MANGANESE ORE

Mine production of manganese ore has expanded more sharply than the production of iron ore despite the fact that both are raw materials for the steel industry. Two factors are responsible — manganese recovery through recycling is very limited, in contrast with the heavy recycling of steel scrap as a substitute for iron ore; and the Soviet Union has reduced the proportion of its manganese output exported to market-economy nations. South Africa has emerged as the leading producer but significant shares of the market have been captured by Australia and Gabon — new producers — and by Brazil, which has greatly expanded its manganese ore industry.

Manganese Ore ('000 t) in 1950			Manganese Ore ('000 t) in 1985		
Country	Output	% of Total	Country	Output	% of Total
India	897	24	South Africa	3,800	29
South Africa	791	21	Brazil	2,400	18
Ghana	723	20	Gabon	2,300	18
Morocco	287	8	Australia	2,100	16
All others	997	27	All others	2,385	18
Aggregate	3,695		Aggregate	12,985	

NICKEL

In 1950 Canada dominated nickel production in the market-economy world. Thanks to aggressive research and market promotion efforts, Canadian producers succeeded in expanding nickel consumption at an average compound rate of 6% during the period to 1973. This growing demand, plus relatively stable prices, attracted interest in the development of nickel resources elsewhere. Consequently, Canada's share of the total market has shrunk drastically, even though its physical output has expanded. The industry now suffers from over-capacity. With public sector firms competing vigorously

Nickel ('000 t) in 1950			Nickel ('000 t) in 1985		
Country	Output	% of Total	Country	Output	% of Total
Canada	112	93	Canada	195	35
New Caledonia	6	5	Australia	81	15
South Africa	1	1	New Caledonia	44	8
United States	1	1	Dominican Rep.	27	5
All others	1	1	All others	210	37
Aggregate	121		Aggregate	557	

for market share, prices in recent years have been unsatisfactory for most producers.

PHOSPHATE ROCK

Phosphate rock is one of three minerals used in huge quantities for soil nutrients, and production has soared in the post-World War II era as food production has increased to keep pace with population growth. The United States and Morocco have maintained their positions as the two principal suppliers, but their combined share of market-economy output has slipped from roughly three-quarters to just under two-thirds in spite of massive production gains. Chapter 7 also comments on phosphate rock.

Phosphate Rock ('000 t) in 1950			Phosphate Rock ('000 t) in 1985		
Country	Output	% of Total	Country	Output	% of Total
United States	10,418	54	United States	51,000	45
Morocco	3,872	20	Morocco	23,000	20
Tunisia	1,525	8	Jordan	7,000	6
Nauru	1,070	6	Tunisia	6,000	6
All others	2,430	13	All others	22,300	20
Aggregate	19,315		Aggregate	112,300	

POTASH

Like phosphate rock, the principal use of potash is in the fertilizer industry. The production figures cited are in K_2O equivalent. In contrast with phosphate rock, where the United States is still by far the world's leading producer, the United States has been surpassed as a potash miner by three other market-economy countries — despite the fact that its 1985 production was at about the same level as in 1950. Canada has emerged as the dominant world producer. More than half the market-economy country aggregate output is extracted

Potash ('000 t) in 1950			Potash ('000 t) in 1985		
Country	Output	% of Total	Country	Output	% of Total
United States	1,168	29	Canada	7,500	57
France	1,108	25	Germany (F.R.)	2,280	17
Germany (F.R.)	912	23	France	1,500	11
Spain	152	4	United States	1,325	10
All others	750	19	All others	2,865	18
Aggregate	4,000		Aggregate	15,470	

from mines in Saskatchewan and New Brunswick. The Federal Republic of Germany (West Germany) and France have for many years been prominent suppliers. Chapter 7 also comments on potash.

ZINC

Remarkable expansion of zinc mine production in Canada has been the outstanding feature of post-war developments in zinc. At the same time, U.S. zinc production has fallen sharply — unlike the pattern followed in the U.S. copper and lead mining industries. This is not due to exhaustion of U.S. zinc resources but rather to a combination of declining ore grades, the obsolescence of much domestic zinc smelting capacity, and cost disadvantages resulting from a strong dollar and heavy environmental control expenditures. Meanwhile Australia, Peru and Mexico have all increased zinc mine output considerably. In addition, Ireland has emerged as a large zinc-mine producer. Abundant zinc resources have been identified in still other countries.

Zinc ('000 t) in 1950			Zinc ('000 t) in 1985		
Country	Output	% of Total	Country	Output	% of Total
United States	566	30	Canada	1,195	24
Canada	284	15	Australia	720	14
Australia	206	11	Peru	560	11
Mexico	224	12	Mexico	310	6
All others	628	33	All others	2,295	45
Aggregate	1,908		Aggregate	5,080	

Prospects of Early Resource Exhaustion are Remote

This is a brief and incomplete summary of trends in production of 10 minerals. Similar trends could be shown for many of the other minerals. Tin has been excluded from this accounting since there is an extended discussion of tin's history in Chapter 6.

The overall impression conveyed by these tabulations is of an era of remarkable expansion of mineral production, based primarily on development of new resources the existence of which was either unknown or only vaguely apparent at the time the Paley Report was published. While mineral resources are finite, the record of growth over a 35-year stretch clearly suggests that prospects of early exhaustion of mineral resources are remote.

Many laymen appear to have the impression that one day, suddenly, resources of a particular mineral may be exhausted, with catastrophic effect on the industries dependent on supplies of that commodity. This will not happen in such dramatic fashion. If and when resources of a specific mineral begin to diminish, prices will gradually increase as it becomes necessary to work lower and still lower grade reserves. As prices rise, alternative materials will be found to substitute for the commodity in short supply. The experience of the tin-mining industry, discussed in Chapter 6, is an example of how the market makes gradual adjustments to resource changes. But, in fact, for almost all minerals required to meet society's needs the current situation is clear. The skill of geologists and mining engineers in locating new deposits has provided more than adequate resources to meet society's current needs.

Some of the significant recent discoveries have been made in what miners call 'elephant country'. By this is meant finds in proximity to existing mining operations in countries with well recognized, favourable geological terrain. Other new additions have been discovered in heavily populated, long settled areas close to major cities. And still others have been found in remote regions. To cite a few examples of such discoveries resulting from the more sophisticated exploration techniques now available to prospectors and geologists, consider the following.

In Chile, a country with a long history of copper production, exploration by private sector firms controlled by foreign investors resumed on a large scale in 1973, after a military junta ousted the leftist Allende régime. Two extraordinary finds have been made in northern Chile since then. One is the extremely rich, although small, high-grade El Indio gold-silver-copper mine brought into production in 1979 by St. Joe Minerals. The other is the large porphyry copper Escondida deposit identified by a consortium of Utah International and Getty Minerals not far from a railroad line and close to the port of Antofagasta. Reserves of several hundred million tons of 2% ore (contrast that with the original Bingham pit venture described on

p. 37) have already been verified, but the property is not yet in production. In 1950 the Paley Report had estimated that Chilean reserves contained 67 million tons of copper. Since then about 23 million tons of copper have been produced. Without additions Chile's reserves would by now have been reduced to 44 million tons. However, in November 1984, the *Engineering & Mining Journal* published an estimate of more than 140 million tons — more than a 100-year reserve at current production rates.

The Tara lead-zinc deposit, situated a few miles from the Irish capital of Dublin, is an outstanding example of a discovery made in close proximity to a metropolitan area of a long-settled country. It was found in the late 1960s after several much smaller deposits had been located in Ireland, a country not previously considered a significant source of minerals. Tara is today the largest zinc-producing mine in western Europe. In 1984 it yielded over 200,000 tons of zinc and about 20,000 tons of lead.

Among major discoveries in remote regions not previously identified as sources of minerals one can cite the Bougainville and Ok Tedi gold-copper-silver deposits in Papua New Guinea; the Polaris mine on Cornwallis Island in the far Arctic north of Canada; and the extraordinary development in the Amazon jungles of Brazil known as Carajas. Here enormous deposits of iron ore, bauxite, manganese ore, and copper have been proved, with iron ore and bauxite already in production. Each of these distant undertakings involves complex problems of transport, power supply, labour availability, housing, and other infrastructure requirements. These make the projects both difficult and highly capital intensive. Nevertheless, the problems have been tackled with great ingenuity. What to many might appear to be intractable difficulties have been overcome.

Resources under the Ocean Deep

More difficult will be the eventual exploitation of vast resources of minerals under the deep oceans or in the frozen Antarctic continent. Since the 1960s the public has been intrigued by the possible extraction of manganese, nickel, cobalt and copper from billions of tons of potato-shaped nodules lying on the ocean floor. The largest concentration of these nodules is in the deep Pacific ocean between the Hawaiian Islands and the North American continent.

For the most part the nodules are 5,000 metres or more below the ocean surface. Pilot work has indicated that they can, in fact, be recovered by ocean mining vessels. They would then be transported by shuttle vessels to land-based processing plants, where the constituent elements could be recovered. But numerous political, economic, and engineering problems must be solved first.

The political problems arise because most of the deposits are in international waters. Who has jurisdiction? How can title be conveyed to the operators of a production project? Considering the huge capital requirements, what protection can an operator have against incursion into its area by another operator?

These questions were debated at great length in a series of United Nations conferences on the Law of the Sea. The proposed Treaty (not accepted by the United States and several other nations) as drafted, provides for the establishment of a public sector international enterprise that might conduct some operations once feasibility had been first established by private sector enterprises.

The Treaty contemplates granting mining rights to a limited number of private concerns. These would be required to pay royalties and also to transfer technology to the international enterprise. No specific arrangements have yet emerged from the Treaty.

Although preliminary investigation has indicated that, in fact, nodules can be recovered from the sea bed and, once recovered, can be processed to produce the constituent metals, the feasibility of large-scale operations remains to be determined. The nodules occur as a thin layer on the ocean bed — perhaps five to ten kilogrammes of nodules per square metre. The assumption has been that to attain a viable undertaking, a single mining vessel will have to extract two million to three million tons of nodules annually. Assuming that five kilogrammes of nodules are mined for each square metre exploited, the individual vessel will have to cover 400 to 600 square kilometres a year. It will have to move in such a fashion that it will not cover the same area twice — a demanding feat of navigation.

Once the nodules are lifted to the ocean surface, they will have to be transferred by the mining vessel to a shuttle vessel that will then transport them to a land-based processing plant. What storage capacity should the mining vessel have? How large should the shuttle vessels be? Precise logistics will have to be worked out so that the mining vessel can be operated continuously and the shuttle vessels do not stand idly by waiting for their cargoes. Ocean storms, machinery breakdowns, periodic dry-docking of the vessels for overhaul, and other contingencies will have to be taken into calculations of costs and outcomes.

Assuming that the political and engineering problems can be managed, the feasibility of mining the manganese nodules still faces serious questions arising from the composition of the nodules themselves and the probable effects of their exploitation on the metals markets.

Analysis indicates that the better quality nodules contain about 25% manganese, 1·5% nickel, 1·2% copper and 0·25% cobalt. Most preliminary economic studies have indicated that manganese recovery may not be viable and that the chief constituent values are in the nickel and the cobalt. Assuming 80% recovery of the contained metals, a ton of nodules would yield 12 kg of nickel, 9·5 kg of copper and 2 kg of cobalt. At prices of $2·50 a pound ($5·5 per kg) for nickel, $0·80 a pound ($1·75 per kg) for copper and $11 a pound ($24·25 per kg) for cobalt, the gross value would be about $130 a ton of nodules, of which over 85% would be represented by the value of the nickel and cobalt.

But the nickel and cobalt markets are relatively small. A single vessel processing two million tons of nodules a year would produce nickel equivalent to 5% of market-economy consumption and cobalt equivalent to 12% of world-economy consumption. Present land-based capacity is quite adequate to meet consumption requirements for both metals. Added capacity arising from exploitation of the ocean resources would lead to weakening markets and lower prices. Moreover, the greater the success of a single ocean project, the greater the prospect that additional projects will be undertaken. Hence uncertainty clouds the prices that will prevail after start-up.

In debating this conundrum, the suggestion was made at the United Nations that ocean-mining capacity be authorized only to meet the anticipated growth in world demand — thereby maintaining the present market for the land-based enterprises. Countries such as Canada for nickel and Zaire and Zambia for cobalt were much concerned over this issue.

The manganese nodules have been recognized as a potential resource for more than 20 years. More recently geologists have identified other major ocean-based non-fuel minerals sources — polymetallic sulphide deposits located in association with active hydrothermal vents found in the Juan de Fuca Ridge of the Pacific off the coast of North America. These deposits are at lesser depths than the manganese nodules and lie within the national jurisdictions of the United States and Mexico. Chile has done some work on similar deposits off its coast and there are believed to be occurrences further north, along the coasts of Colombia, Ecuador and Peru. In the Red Sea somewhat similar deposits have been the target of work done under the jurisdiction of Saudi Arabia.

The polymetallic sulphide deposits have copper, zinc and silver as their chief constituent metal values. These metals have broader markets than nickel and cobalt. Any addition to supply always affects markets, but the broader the market the less the disruption. For these reasons it is thought exploitation of the polymetallic sulphides probably would have a less pronounced impact on prices than exploitation of manganese nodules. The fact that the deposits lie within national zones lessens the political difficulties of initiating operations. The lesser depths may tend to ease the engineering problems.

Nevertheless, the financing of ventures to mine polymetallic deposits seems likely to await favourable economic conditions in the markets.

In still another category is the Antarctic continent. The limited work done there under difficult conditions has identified copper, molybdenum, nickel and chromium deposits as well as fuels. Some 12 nations lay claim to parts of the Antarctic continent. Many of the claims overlap. However, by Treaty signed in 1959 the nations have agreed that so long as it remains in force "No acts or activities taking place . . . shall constitute a basis for asserting, supporting or denying a claim to territorial sovereignty in Antarctica."

Meanwhile, a United Nations staff study suggested the formation of an international committee to consider issues such as mineral development. This will involve problems similar to those discussed at the Law of the Sea conferences — with countries other than the 12 Treaty signatories doubtless maintaining that development should be undertaken by an international agency under the 'Common Heritage of Mankind' philosophy.

The resources embodied in the manganese nodules, the poly-metallic sulphides and the Antarctic deposits are unlikely to be important sources of minerals in the early future. However, the very fact that they exist provides reassurance that lasting shortages of most non-fuel minerals will not develop in the foreseeable future.

Meanwhile, land-based deposits in presently populated areas have proven to have vastly greater resources than was believed to be the case in 1950, and the potential for further extension is great.

CHAPTER THREE

Money for Minerals

Inherent Risks in Mineral Investments

Great success attended exploration for new non-fuel mineral deposits in the years after World War II. The fear that resources would be insufficient to satisfy the world's appetite was laid to rest — at least for the balance of this century and, in the opinion of many, for a much longer time.

But discovery of mineral resources is only a first step. Before minerals can be made available to meet consuming needs, substantial sums must be invested in opening mines, building processing facilities, and providing the supporting infrastructure that assures adequate transportation, power, housing and other needed facilities.

When considering new mineral projects investors face a myriad of uncertainties. What will be the future demand for the product? Will other firms also be starting new projects, raising the spectre of potential over-capacity? How competitive will the new venture's costs be? What is likely to happen to product prices? What risks are contained in the political or military environment?

There are no certain answers — only assumptions. Even the most sophisticated and experienced investor may make serious miscalculations. The petroleum industry's experience with copper investments is an example.

Some years ago many leading oil-producing firms concluded that the copper mining industry of the United States provided attractive opportunities to capitalize on their exploration and operating expertise. Unlike the steel and aluminium industries, where investment is predominantly in processing, the copper industry's fortunes are primarily tied to the discovery and exploitation of mineral resources. Managements of oil companies saw in this a symbiotic relationship with their own industry.

Beginning in the late fifties cash-rich oil firms began to acquire copper properties. To obtain their foothold in the industry, they offered prices to shareholders of the independent copper companies far above previously prevailing stock market quotations. By 1980 well over half of all U.S. copper mine capacity had been absorbed by oil companies.

Disillusion set in during the early eighties. The rising demand and satisfactory profits that had been enjoyed by the copper industry in previous years melted away in the face of world recession. Copper prices plunged as over-production built up inventories at refineries and in commodity exchange warehouses.

By 1983 United States mines were suffering staggering losses. Oil company owners scrambled to divest themselves of their copper holdings. Some mines were sold; other mines were spun off to struggle on again as independent entities; and still other properties were shut down with 'For Sale' signs prominently, if to date unsuccessfully, displayed.

Oil companies sustained losses amounting to billions of dollars as a consequence of having paid high prices for their copper investments shortly before a severe downturn in copper prices. Other investors have been more fortunate in their investment timing or more astute in identifying opportunities. Fortunes have been made as well as lost in minerals.

Characteristics of the minerals industry which must be considered in making investment decisions include:

1. Mining operations are subject to world pricing. The products of one producer are essentially fungible with the identical products of its competitors. Unlike manufactured products, questions of style and brand preference (which enable manufacturers to maintain prices independently of their competitors at most times) have little relevance in the marketing of minerals. Buyers are motivated primarily by price considerations.

2. Mining has always been a capital intensive business. In the past two

decades capital costs of new mineral projects have soared spectacu-
larly, far outstripping the rate of inflation.

3. Demand for minerals is volatile. During upturns in the business
cycle it rises more steeply than the average of industrial activity.
During downturns in the business cycle it falls more precipitously
than the average of industrial activity. The pattern of demand for
aluminium and copper during the years 1973-77, shown in Chart 2
(page 20), provides a clear demonstration.

4. By contrast, changes in supply are relatively sluggish. Mine
managements prefer to operate their properties at maximum rates of
output in order to achieve economies of scale. High capital costs and
high overhead costs tend to be fixed. Hence the cost per unit of
production is lowest when it is divided by the largest feasible volume
of output. Thus, even though sales volume may slacken in periods of
economic recession, managements are reluctant to change operating
rates.

5. Hence, visible stocks of minerals rise significantly during business
downturns and are sharply reduced when demand increases. These
inventory fluctuations are the root cause of the unstable and
unpredictable price behaviour of many minerals. Unstable prices in
turn mean that the profits and losses of mining firms follow highly
erratic patterns that contrast unfavourably with the financial outcomes of less cyclically vulnerable industries.

6. Traditionally, mining projects were financed either by drawing on
retained earnings or by sale of equity. Since the mid-sixties this has
changed dramatically. Because of reduced earnings and soaring
capital costs, mining companies have increasingly resorted to funded
debt to finance expansion. In the mid-sixties and through the early
seventies, banks and other lenders had access to abundant funds.
They competed eagerly to finance mining projects. Following the
energy crisis of 1974, the changed economic environment in the
mineral markets caused them to scrutinize such projects more
conservatively. As for equity investments, the new high-tech industries looked more attractive to risk-taking entrepreneurs.

7. Political risks for private investors considering mineral projects
have increased. In several instances governments have insisted on

re-negotiation of concession arrangements after production has begun. In other cases, exchange controls have been imposed, limiting or prohibiting repatriation of profits to foreign investors. New discriminatory tax measures have been enacted by some countries. In some cases of expropriation, private investors have found they have limited scope for negotiating equitable arrangements with sovereign governments. Added to unfavourable market developments, these political uncertainties have acted to reduce the flow of private funds into many countries.

8. An increasing share of mineral production, particularly in the developing countries, is now in the hands of state controlled organizations. These have access to financial assistance from international lending institutions established to promote their industrial diversification. In some instances financing has been obtained for projects that private sector companies would not have considered viable.

Later chapters will deal in detail with the price uncertainties prevailing in most mineral markets. The following describes relative aspects on some of the other investment considerations in a minerals industry context.

Mining is Capital Intensive

To achieve a given level of sales revenue, a mining project requires more capital than a venture of comparable size in either manufacturing or the retail trade. This means that miners need a greater profit margin on sales revenues than manufacturers or merchants to obtain a commensurate return on investment. In recent years inflationary trends have driven up the capital requirements of all industries but capital requirements of the mineral industries have increased explosively. Why is this?

Lower grades of ore are being mined. This requires the extraction and treatment of larger tonnages of raw material to secure a given quantity of final product. The amount of capital invested is more closely related to the gross tonnage of ore to be handled than to the net amounts of mineral product sold.

TABLE 3: CAPITAL COSTS OF COPPER MINE AND MILL PROJECTS

Mine	Location	Date of Start-Up	Initial Annual Capacity*	Cost of Facilities $	Cost per ton of Capacity $	Avg. Price of Copper Year of Start-Up† $	Ratio of Investment to Revenue
Silver Bell	Ariz., U.S.	1953	18,000	18,000,000	1,000	635 — US	1·58
Tyrone	N.M., U.S.	1969	50,000	118,000,000	2,360	1,048 — US	2·25
Andina	Chile	1970	58,000	139,000,000	2,400	1,411 — LME	1·70
Lornex	B.C., Canada	1972	54,000	138,000,000	2,555	1,070 — LME	2·38
Caridad	Mexico	1980	140,000	673,000,000	4,800	2,189 — LME	2·19
Copper Flat	N.M., U.S.	1982	18,000	103,000,000	5,720	1,607 — US	3·55
Tintaya	Peru	1985	52,000	326,000,000	6,270	1,408 — LME	4·45
COPPER MINE, MILL AND SMELTER PROJECTS‡							
Toquepala	Peru	1959	132,000	237,000,000	1,800	670 — LME	2·69
Cuajone	Peru	1976	162,000	726,000,000	4,480	1,412 — LME	3·17
Sar Cheshmeh	Iran	1982	145,000	1,400,000,000	9,655	1,482 — LME	6·51

* In terms of copper content of concentrates or blister produced, tons.

† As quoted in ABMS yearbook, LME prices converted at average rate for sterling. Note this is price for refined copper. Mines must absorb smelting and refining charges deducted from price for refined copper. By product revenues are an offset. This is a significant factor, particularly for Lornex and Tintaya.

‡ Capacities stated in tons of copper content of blister.

Consumers demand stricter specifications with fewer impurities in the minerals and metals they buy. This means miners have to have more elaborate flowsheets and must install more equipment related to quality controls.

As wage rates have risen, increased mechanization becomes an attractive alternative. This reduces the man-hours worked per unit of product and cuts operating costs, but it requires a larger initial investment.

Capital requirements have been increased by laws dealing with the environment and with safety. Tighter air and water pollution regulations require facilities that are costly to buy and to operate. They do not add to effective capacity. The burden falls more heavily on mineral producers in countries with stringent environmental regulations.

Infrastructure, particularly for projects in remote regions, is essential. Provision must be made for transport, power, housing and community facilities. In some instances a share of these costs may be met by government, but in other cases the entire cost of infrastructure devolves on the operating company.

To illustrate how capital investment has increased, Table 3 lists 10 copper projects launched during the period 1953-85. Other minerals have experienced similar trends. (The writer contributed a paper to Mintek 50, published in 1985, citing figures for gold, silver, molybdenum, nickel, lead and zinc projects.) The copper experience may be taken as representative.

In the table the figures are stated in United States' dollars. Currencies of the other principal copper producing countries (Chile, Canada, Zambia, Zaire, Peru, etc.) have all declined in value in relation to the dollar during the period covered. Thus, investment costs in terms of the currencies of those countries would show even greater increases.

Of the 10 projects enumerated, three included the provision of smelting capacity. The seven others carried processing only through to the stage of concentrate. Since the value of copper contained in blister (the intermediate metallic form resulting from smelting) is greater than the value of copper contained in concentrate, this helps to offset the greater investment per ton of capacity for projects involving smelters.

The table lists the location of each project, the year of initial production, the initial capacity (in several cases subsequently expanded), the initial gross investment, the investment per ton of annual copper capacity, the appropriate average price of copper for the year of initial production and the consequent ratio of the investment per ton of copper to that price. For the U.S. projects, the average price used is the *Metals Week* domestic producer price in the year of start-up. For the projects outside the U.S., the average price used is the London Metal Exchange settlement price (converted to U.S. dollars) in the year of start-up.

This use of the historical price of copper at the time production started is an effort to offset the influence of inflation on capital costs. Thus, the average price of copper in 1953, when the first project began operations, was less than half the average price in 1985, when the most recent project started up. Yet, if the price of copper more than doubled during the 32-year span, the amount invested per ton of copper capacity increased six-fold. In relation to revenue the true increase in capital costs may be said to have been three-fold rather than six-fold.

Obviously fluctuating prices affect the comparison. The project that started up in 1980, a year of relatively high copper prices, had a more favourable ratio of investment to revenue in that year than did the 1985 project. Since copper mines typically have a productive life span of 20 years or more, the profitability of the investment will be determined not by the outcome in the first year (when prices may be abnormally high or abnormally low) but over the entire life of the mine.

Management, therefore, must endeavour to forecast probable product prices over an extended period. So far as possible, the decision should not be overly influenced by temporary price conditions prevailing at the time of the feasibility study. This is no easy task, however, and many projects have been launched on the basis of overly optimistic price expectations during brief periods of booming markets.

What return should be expected on an investment? Considering the risks inherent in mining, most private sector managements look for a return of at least 15% or more on new funds committed — whether the source be equity or funded debt. Public sector companies tend to have different motives and their decisions are often based on considerations other than return on investment.

To obtain a return of 15% on new investment, if $2 of capital is required to produce $1 of annual revenue, then the profit margin must be 30 cents on each $1 of sales. If the investment is as much as $4 for each $1 of annual revenue (note some figures in the table), then to obtain a 15% return, the profit margin must be 60 cents on each $1 of sales revenue — a margin rarely attained.

Sources of Funds

Table 4 illustrates the increasing use of borrowed money by the mineral industry in recent years. It shows the rising tide of funded debt experienced by nine United States' mining companies during the years 1964-76. All nine companies were engaged in copper production but many were also producers of other minerals — including aluminium, coal, lead, zinc, iron, molybdenum and precious metals.

During the 12 year span, aggregate debt of the nine companies increased from $252 million at the end of 1964 to $3,204 million at the end of 1976. Later figures cannot be compiled, because five of the nine companies ceased to be independent after 1976. Separate balance sheets have not been available since the mergers. Anaconda, Copper Range, Cyprus and Kennecott all became subsidiaries of oil companies. Inspiration was acquired by a corporation controlled by a South African mining firm.

Of the nine companies, two had no funded debt in 1964. Those that did have long-term debt obligations that year showed a low proportion of debt to equity. During the years after World War II and before 1964 all nine companies had made substantial capital investments. These were largely funded by drawing on their substantial working capital positions or by using profits and other sources of cash in excess of dividend disbursements.

TABLE 4: LONG-TERM DEBT POSITION OF NINE U.S. MINERAL COMPANIES

(Figures in $U.S. million)

Company	1964	1965	1966	1967	1968	1969	1970	1971	1972	1973	1974	1975	1976
Amax	81	108	126	157	190	201	260	391	457	441	400	535	630
Asarco	41	40	36	35	34	24	24	38	51	92	116	342	400
Anaconda	93	79	65	128	277	306	367	392	278	252	274	336	502
Copper Range	25	24	22	35	33	28	24	36	35	34	33	31	29
Cyprus Mines	5	11	13	29	18	54	40	35	22	17	10	114	214
Inspiration	0	0	0	1	1	1	1	1	19	50	46	40	34
Kennecott	5	0	26	16	233	195	178	315	269	221	226	406	540
Newmont	0	0	0	0	0	47	108	202	224	218	209	251	294
Phelps Dodge	2	0	0	3	29	77	86	166	181	282	327	523	561
Aggregate*	252	262	289	404	815	932	1,089	1,575	1,537	1,606	1,643	2,579	3,204

* Totals may not be exact, due to rounding of fractions of million. Figures are as of Dec. 31 of each year.

Principal mineral involvements of companies during this period. **Amax** — molybdenum, coal, iron ore, copper, lead, zinc, potash, nickel, precious metals. **Asarco** — copper, silver, zinc, lead, minor metals, gold, coal, titanium. **Anaconda** — copper, aluminium, silver, zinc, lead, minor metals. **Copper Range** — copper, gold. **Cyprus Mines** — copper, industrial minerals, zinc, lead, molybdenum. **Inspiration** — copper, silver. **Kennecott** — copper, coal, titanium, precious metals, molybdenum.

Newmont — copper, gold, oil, manganese, lithium, coal, nickel. **Phelps Dodge** — copper, aluminium, uranium, precious metals. Copper Range, Cyprus and Inspiration properties were predominantly in the United States. The remaining companies had substantial properties and/or investments outside the United States in Canada, Latin America, Australia and Africa.

Source: Company annual reports.

Between 1964 and 1974 all nine companies were profitable. Thus, during those years their increased debts were not due to financial reverses. Rather, they borrowed because the pace of capital expenditures accelerated. In addition to expansion of their existing businesses and diversification into new fields, they were also faced with new requirements — notably the need to expend large sums on environmental control equipment to meet stringent regulations imposed by government. Moreover, as inflation drove up prices of equipment, the cash flow generated through depreciation on older facilities was inadequate to cover the cost of replacements.

The severe recession of 1975 and 1976 exacerbated the problem. The aggregate debt of the nine companies doubled in those two years. Furthermore, soaring interest rates made the burden of this new debt substantially greater than that imposed by earlier borrowings.

Thus, an industry that had been highly solvent in 1964 was heavily indebted by the end of 1976. The U.S. industry's ability to compete with overseas miners was seriously impaired by interest costs as well as by the expense of meeting environmental regulations. A temporary respite developed in 1979 and 1980, when copper prices briefly strengthened, but the advent of another severe recession in 1981 put new pressures on the four remaining independent companies.

As for the five companies that had been swallowed up in the era of acquisitions, reference has already been made to the dissatisfaction of their new owners with those investments.

The experience of the U.S. copper industry was not unique. In varying degrees similar difficulties faced many of the private sector producers of other minerals. In recent years, the news pages of the trade and financial press have carried a disturbing record of plant closures, corporate reorganizations, and other changes dictated by financial stringency.

The Emergence of Public Sector Companies

Sweeping changes have occurred in the control of mineral production since 1950. Then, private sector corporations were the dominant factor in the world's mineral industries.

Private corporations representing United States, British, Belgian, Dutch, Canadian and South African capital not only owned and operated mineral enterprises in the industrialized nations, but they also controlled much of the output of minerals in the developing countries of the Third World.

Today's industry structure is very different. Changes in control occurred both in the newly independent lands that had been colonies of the industrialized nations and in developing countries that had been politically independent but whose mineral industries had been dominated by foreign capital.

It is not hard to understand why these changes happened. Mineral resources are considered part of the national heritage. Control of that heritage by foreigners is seen as depriving the state and its citizens of revenues and profits to which they are rightfully entitled. In many instances, politicians made speeches charging that foreign companies had deliberately understated the value of exports and profits in order to transfer wealth abroad. To correct this, they proposed to seize control of the mineral industry.

In many cases mineral properties were nationalized — tin mines in Bolivia and Indonesia, bauxite deposits in Guyana, copper mines in Zaire and Chile. In other instances the governments negotiated for a share ownership (usually over 50%), sometimes paying cash and in other instances taking shares in lieu of royalty or taxes. In some countries — Brazil and Mexico are examples — legislation was adopted to encourage the sale of control by private sector foreign firms to private sector national firms.

On newer projects, in some instances joint venture arrangements were worked out between the host governments and private firms, whether national or foreign. Sometimes these involved technical and operating management by the private sector investors, with broad policy direction and marketing responsibility exercised by the government.

Several academic students of the industry have strongly advocated arrangements under which ownership of mineral resources is held by the host government with foreign multi-national firms providing experienced management in exchange for liberal fees.

66

At least two major industrialized mineral exporting countries — Canada and Australia — have also manifested nationalist tendencies. To reduce foreign control of domestic mineral deposits, they have required expatriate investors to seek out domestic partners. Tax incentives and export controls have been devised to foster local processing of minerals instead of exporting raw materials.

During the sixties and early seventies politicians claimed that they had at last wrested for the local population the share of mineral riches to which they were entitled. More recently a degree of disillusionment has set in among Third World governments. Like the oil companies, to whom reference has already been made, they have learned that markets for minerals are unpredictable. Revenues and profits derived from mineral activities since 1974 have fallen far short of expectations. Funds to finance new projects are not readily available to debt-ridden governments. Many existing mines have run at substantial losses.

As a consequence many governments of developing nations are once again offering inducements to foreign private investors to bring in fresh capital for mineral projects.

A typical example is the Chilean copper industry. The Frei Government of Chile in the late sixties had negotiated with the U.S. owners to acquire interests in the country's four largest copper mines. When the leftist Allende régime took office in 1970 it expropriated these properties. Modest compensation was offered for one recently completed mine but none was offered for the three other mines on the grounds that the foreign companies had already earned excessive profits. When the right-wing military junta under General Pinochet took over, a new corporation, Codelco, was formed to operate the mines for the government but compensation for all properties was negotiated with the former owners to reassure foreign investors of equitable treatment.

Codelco has succeeded in expanding production. The government has allowed that company to retain a substantial share of its foreign exchange revenues to finance capital expenditures. Competent Chilean technicians are operating the properties without the assistance of expatriate experts.

However, several major identified copper deposits, as yet not in production, exist in Chile. The Pinochet Government has adopted an investment code to induce private investors to develop these properties and has issued assurances that their tenure will be secure.

In some other countries public sector firms have been unable to maintain the levels of production attained under private ownership. Bolivia, one of the first countries to expropriate mineral properties, took over its three largest tin mining operations in the early fifties. Production has declined precipitously since then. Huge financial losses have been sustained even though, for much of the time, tin prices have out-performed prices of other base metals. By contrast, the smaller mines in the country that remained in private hands have been more successful in maintaining production, despite the highly inflationary conditions under which they have worked.

The Zambian copper industry has not been able to duplicate the achievements of the Chilean industry. A basic problem has been the shortage of technical experts. Many expatriate engineers have left the country and not enough Zambian nationals have been trained to replace them. The country's acute shortage of foreign exchange has meant the government has been unwilling to earmark sufficient funds to purchase needed equipment or spare parts for the copper mines. Production has been gradually declining, new reserves have not been developed, and the outlook for Zambian copper is considered gloomy by many.

Indeed, public sector corporations in general have not devoted much effort to exploration for new mineral deposits. One reason of course is that unfavourable mineral markets have left them short of cash. Because they acquired promising but as yet undeveloped deposits from the former expatriate owners, their managements have had little incentive to try to find still more reserves. In addition, they recognize that the capital cost of expanding production at an existing mine with good reserves is markedly less than the cost of launching new 'greenfields' projects with expensive requirements for infrastructure.

Thus, with some exceptions, most public sector mineral undertakings are exploiting deposits previously discovered by private enterprise. This strategy maximizes current revenues and employment, even though there may be unfavourable implications for the long-term existence of the mineral industry in the particular country.

On the other hand, public sector firms have aggressively increased domestic capacity to process mineral raw materials. Mineral exporting countries have long deplored what they consider to be an inferior role as suppliers of unprocessed raw materials to the major consuming nations. By establishing domestic capacity to process ores and concentrates, they can increase employment and enhance foreign exchange earnings. Moreover, the existence of domestic metallurgical and chemical industries may encourage the development of downstream manufacturing facilities, thereby adding to national industrialization.

It has not been difficult for developing countries to finance projects for processing capacity. In addition to international organizations such as the World Bank and the various regional development banks, most governments of industrialized countries have created national institutions to provide loans for projects that will increase their machinery exports or obtain engineering and construction assignments for their contracting firms.

As a result, numerous projects have gone forward in the developing countries to provide alumina and aluminium plants, copper, lead, zinc, nickel and tin smelters, installations to convert chrome and manganese ores to ferro-manganese and ferro-chrome and chemical facilities to produce agricultural fertilizers from phosphate, potash, sulphur and other indigenous resources.

Lending institutions apparently regard processing facilities as less risky than new mining projects, which are considered speculative because of uncertainties about grades and tonnages of ore deposits and the extreme oscillations of mineral prices. Yet although some processing projects in developing countries have turned out well, in other cases the investments have not been viable. Ore reserves have proved insufficient to provide assured feed for the plant, or capital and operating costs have proved excessive. Thus, aggregate costs may exceed the costs experienced when ores or concentrates were exported to foreign processors.

An example of the pitfalls in such projects is provided by the Karachipampa lead-tin-zinc project in Bolivia. The plant was built in 1983 at a reported cost of $126 million with funds provided by German and Belgian banks. They made the loans to secure machinery exports and/or engineering and construction contracts for their nationals. Bolivian lead concentrates had previously been exported for smelting abroad. To provide employment and enhance product value, the smelter was designed with a rated capacity of 24,000 tons of lead, 800 tons of tin, 3,300 tons of zinc and 500 tons of copper annually, plus a by-product yield of some silver, bismuth and antimony.

But at prices prevailing in 1983 insufficient feed was available to run the plant, which remained idle for more than two years, while interest costs mounted and equipment deteriorated. Meanwhile, like other Latin-American countries, Bolivia suffered agonizing inflation and an inability to cope with a huge debt burden.

Table 5 indicates that at fairly liberal estimates of price (including a generous allowance for value of by-products) the gross value of the plant's production might be $35 million annually — a capital to revenue ratio of 3·6 to 1. This gross value of product must also cover

TABLE 5: REVENUE ESTIMATES FOR A BOLIVIAN PROCESSING PLANT — KARACHIPAMPA

Commodity	Quantity Tons	Assumed Price* $	Gross Revenue $
Lead	24,000	500	12,000,000
Tin	800	12,000	9,600,000
Zinc	3,300	800	2,640,000
Copper	500	2,000	1,000,000
Silver, Bismuth, Antimony	unstated	various	10,000,000
Total sales value at assumed prices			35,240,000

Reported capital investment was $126 million.

Capacity information based on article appearing in *American Metal Market* in July, 1985.

Assumed prices are for refined metal delivered to consuming points in North America or Europe. Some production will be contained in intermediate products requiring ongoing refining elsewhere as Karachipampa is basically a lead smelter and refinery.

* These prices are above the average levels prevailing in late 1985, early 1986.

the prices paid to miners for the raw material feed, the expense of delivering the product to market, and the cost of refining those metals contained in intermediate products — since it is not clear that all products can be carried through to the refined stage at Karachipampa. After these deductions the remaining revenues are unlikely to be adequate to cover both operating costs and the interest expense and amortization on borrowed capital.

The motives leading to the construction of Karachipampa are clear — a desire by the Bolivian officials involved to provide employment, reduce dependence on foreign processors, and diversify the economy, while the foreign lenders and contractors were eager to export machinery and obtain the building contracts. While increased employment and greater earnings of foreign exchange are legitimate aims, the pitfalls of the project are equally clear — an excessive investment in relation to the probable revenue stream, inadequate assurance of raw material feed, and a plant too small to compete in world markets where the efficient competitors benefit from economies of scale.

Karachipampa is illustrative, not exceptional. Similar motives have underlain many projects for processing facilities in developing countries that have eventually created financial problems for the host countries. The capital intensive nature of such projects means that they involve large debts in return for relatively limited employment opportunities and minor additions to foreign exchange flows.

For most developing countries, labour intensive projects will create more lasting benefits than capital intensive projects — as the countries of southeast Asia have clearly demonstrated in recent years. Their superior economic performance in comparison with the countries of Africa and Latin America is not unrelated to the priority they have given to development of labour intensive activities.

Political Risks for the Private Investor

As developing countries turn once again to foreign investors to play a role in the exploitation of their mineral resources, private sector managements must necessarily weigh the risks of committing funds

71

beyond those already invested abroad. The events of the post-war era clearly indicate the need for caution. Although some companies prefer to avoid being involved, others are prepared to continue making foreign investments, provided they can see a way by which to minimize the political risks.

In pre-war days, many private sector firms strove to obtain 100% ownership of promising mineral deposits abroad — only to find in the post-war era that they were politically exposed and vulnerable to takeover. As a result, few executives today wish to go it alone on foreign projects. The preference is to form joint ventures with other private sector concerns, sometimes with participation on a minority basis by the host government.

Whether the host government is actually an equity participant or whether its stake in the venture is in the form of royalties and/or taxes, modern operators are always conscious of government intent. The days have passed when private management unilaterally decided on questions of operating rates, labour policies, new capital investment, or marketing strategy. Governments expect a voice in all such decisions before they are made.

In recent joint venture arrangements many of the larger undertakings have involved private sector companies from several different countries. The rationale for such arrangements is that host governments are more likely to be cautious in dealing with investors from several different nations than in dealing with investors of a single nationality.

Similarly, in borrowing funds for new projects, the effort is usually made to borrow from banks in several countries as well as from international institutions. Governments are chary about making moves that impair their credit ratings if several of the principal capital markets are involved.

Despite the existence of mining codes or other regulations defining a government's policy in dealing with foreign investment, investors undertaking major projects frequently find it wise to negotiate a bilateral agreement setting forth the conditions under which they are prepared to commit funds. Usually such agreements cover a stated period — typically the time required to pay off the original debt and recapture the equity investment. Thereafter, the project becomes subject to the general regulations governing mineral operations.

Because many developing countries levy high rates of import duty on machinery (not as a protectionist device but as a means of collecting revenue), frequently the bilateral agreement provides for the waiving of such duties which would otherwise add considerably to the capital cost of the programme. Another area that requires careful definition is the treatment of foreign exchange earned by the project after start-up of production. Private sector managements seek assurance that they will have the foreign currency needed to buy supplies, pay salaries to expatriates, and discharge debt obligations. Repatriation of funds for dividends is also a significant topic for inclusion.

However carefully drawn such agreements may be, the investor can never forget that he is dealing with a sovereign government. During the period of negotiation, the host government is anxious to attract capital to its industry and is prepared to offer inducements to ensure completion of the investment. Once the project has emerged from the construction phase into actual operation, a subtle shift occurs in the balance of power. Now the investor is committed; the funds have been spent.

Not infrequently the host government will request a re-negotiation of terms — sometimes on the grounds that conditions have changed radically since the original agreement was made. An example of this was the agreement negotiated in 1967 between Bougainville Copper and the Government of Papua New Guinea, at a time when that country was a territory under the control of Australia. The mine began production in 1972 and was immediately profitable. One major contributing factor was the rising price of gold — which had been $US35 an ounce when the agreement was made. In 1973 the mine made a profit of $A158 million, a better than 40% return in a single year on the original investment. By then Papua New Guinea was an independent country. Its government demanded a re-negotiation of the 1967 agreement and this was done in 1974, providing *inter alia* for a substantial increase in maximum income tax to a peak rate of 70% of all income in excess of a 15% return on the original investment.

Because governments of developing countries have harboured deep suspicions that commodity prices are manipulated by the consumer countries, a frequent demand by such governments is that they control the marketing of exported minerals, even though produced by private sector companies. The Peruvian military junta that took control in that country in 1968 expropriated some mineral properties but it allowed most of the industry to remain in private hands. However, it decreed that all mineral exports would be marketed by a government corporation formed for the purpose. This led to friction and confusion as sales contracts were negotiated that did not always coincide with the realities of production and transport availability. Moreover the government corporation assessed sales commissions well in excess of the companies' previous selling costs.

Controversy and disagreement seem inevitably to be involved at the interface between government and the private sector — no matter how anxious both parties may be to maintain good relations. Mention has already been made that several learned academic consultants have suggested a possible solution to the problems of producing minerals from deposits located in developing countries would be for ownership to rest with the host government but actual operation to be in the hands of an experienced international mining firm which would be paid a generous management fee. On the face of it, this seems a sensible arrangement.

However, in the few instances where such arrangements have been tried, difficulties have arisen. If a generous fee is agreed by the host government this will inevitably attract strong criticism from opposition politicians who are prone to suggest corruption on the part of the government officials originally involved. Or if inflation drives up commodity prices and the fee is based on a percentage of production or sales the officials who negotiated the agreement may later demand a drop in the rate of fee. On the other hand, if the fee is modest, the multinational firm will see no advantage in undertaking the task of running someone else's properties, using senior management time and effort, and often helping to create competition for itself.

The Sar Cheshmeh project in Iran was originally cited as a model of such arrangements. The Shah's government negotiated two contracts

74

— one with engineering contractors to build the project and a second with a major mining company to operate it after construction. As shown in Table 3, the cost per ton of capacity for Sar Cheshmeh was more than double the cost of the Cuajone project in Peru, completed a few years earlier, giving rise to the suspicion that the contractor had not exercised stringent control over capital costs since it was not investing its own funds. The plant had barely been completed when revolution developed, the Shah was overthrown, and the project stood idle for several years. It is now in production but firm data are not available as to the rate of operation. The belief has been that production has been at a rate far below the designated plant capacity. In any case, production is in the hands of the Iranians and not under the management of the mining company originally engaged.

This appears to be a litany of difficulties and hazards for private sector mining firms considering investments in the developing world. However, despite the existence of problems, some companies have been able to develop a *modus vivendi* with their host governments. This is particularly true of the major London based mining houses — and also of Anglo American, the largest of the South African mining conglomerates. Major Japanese mining concerns have been aggressive in negotiating with developing country governments for exploration rights and participation in new ventures. In most cases they appear to prefer to take part through long-term purchase contracts or technical operating arrangements for metallurgical plants, rather than through equity investment. Apparently lack of experience in large tonnage mining operations is a deterrent. The French have largely confined their interest to Africa and the Iberian peninsula in Europe. Canadian mining firms have been active in Spain, Greenland, Brazil and, of course, Australia.

As for the United States, Latin America was long a prime field for investment for the base-metal companies but, as previously noted, many of them have been acquired by oil companies. In recent years the large U.S. aluminium firms have taken participations in virtually all the overseas bauxite developments in the Caribbean, Brazil, Guinea and Australia. They are active participants in schemes to add alumina and aluminium processing capacity throughout the world.

75

CHAPTER FOUR

Prices of Minerals

Mark Twain once said that everybody talks about the weather but nobody does anything about it. The pricing of minerals is like that — a great topic for conversation but a difficult subject for effective action. In the long run no one — not individual companies, not cartels, not governments — has been able to control prices effectively, with one possible exception, which is examined in Chapter 6.

Yet prices are central to the outcome of every mineral enterprise. If the price of the mineral produced is less than the cost of production, losses are certain. Increasing the volume of sales simply increases the losses sustained. Regardless of the quantity and quality of reserves in a given deposit, its viability hinges on the relationship between the price received for the product and the cost of production.

Hence, when entrepreneurs consider whether exploitation of a newly developed mineral deposit is warranted, inevitably they must estimate the prices at which its output will be sold. And since in most cases a time lag of several years will elapse between the decision to proceed and the actual inception of production, forecasting prices is no simple task.

Indeed, in recent years turbulent and volatile markets have defied the analytical skills of the most experienced students of mineral markets. Thanks to the availability of computers, increasingly elaborate procedures have been devised to predict future prices. These include detailed projections of future supply and demand on a global basis, assumptions as to production costs of competitive suppliers, technological changes in production and consumption, possible development of substitute materials and estimates of the

political environment, world-wide. All these appraisals are necessarily highly tentative and subject to unforeseen developments.
Managements are well aware of the tenuous nature of the price
forecasts. *Yet, tenuous or not, any investment plan for a new mineral
enterprise must make assumptions as to the prices at which its
production will be sold.*

Methods Used to Establish Mineral Prices

Quite apart from the difficulty of forecasting prices, those new to the
minerals industries are likely to find the way in which prices of
minerals are established confusing, complex and contentious.

Pricing of minerals is confusing because no uniform yardstick exists
for measuring prices. Other aspects of a mineral undertaking are
readily measured by known standards. Production is measured in
ounces, pounds or tons. Labour efficiency can be measured by hours,
days or weeks worked. Power consumption can be tallied in
kilowatt-hours. Transportation problems are related to distances,
measured in miles or kilometres. These are unvarying standards.
They are the same today as they were a hundred or a thousand years
ago. Not so with prices.

Prices are measured in currencies. The value of currencies is not
constant. If the current price of copper, for instance, expressed in
cents per pound, appears to be exactly the same as it was 10 years ago,
in fact it is not the same — because during the 10 years that have
elapsed inflation has eroded the value of the currency received. To
adjust for inflation an effort is sometimes made to compensate by
using a 'deflator' — which means recalculating prices based on the
purchasing power of currency in a stated base year. But economists
differ widely as to which index is to be used in making such
calculations and in choosing the base year for purposes of comparisons.

And, what is even more confusing, the value of any given currency
in relation to other currencies is likely to be different today from the
value it had in relation to those same currencies in the past. During
the years between 1944 and 1971 most currencies were measured in

relation to gold, the value of which was fixed at $US35 per ounce under the Bretton Woods arrangements that established the International Monetary Fund. Changes in exchange rates were relatively infrequent. After 1971, however, this relative stability gave way to floating exchange rates with frequent and sometimes violent fluctuations.

For internationally traded commodities, the result can be bewildering. Thus, the average price of copper in 1984, expressed in dollars, was lower than the average price in 1983. But, expressed in pounds sterling, the 1984 average price of copper was higher than in 1983. What was the real trend in copper prices in 1984? Did they rise or did they fall? (see Chart 4, p.96).

The divergence of course was the consequence of the strength of the dollar in relation to the pound. Or should one say that it was the consequence of the weakness of the pound sterling in relation to the dollar?

This is an exercise in semantics akin to the old saw about describing water in a glass — is the glass half full or is it half empty?

Pricing of minerals is complex because each mineral has evolved a unique pattern. Hundreds of mineral commodities enter into commerce today. Differences exist as to quantity and quality specifications, points of delivery, payment terms, pricing periods and a host of other factors. These differences arise from the nature of the production and/or consumption of the particular commodity and, in some cases, from long traditions with obscure origins.

Even with respect to a single commodity, pricing practices will vary depending on the national market served. In some countries prices are quoted in pounds or short tons, while in others the same commodity may be quoted in kilogrammes or metric tons.

For some minerals marketed in ore form the price may vary with the quantity of the element contained — as is normally the case for most ferro-alloy ores — while in other instances the price is based on gross weight — as in the instance of bauxite.

Pricing of minerals is contentious. Everyone professes a desire to use methods that result in fair, reasonable, and stable prices but wide disagreement prevails on how this result can best be obtained. At least four major methods of establishing prices are currently employed within the minerals industries:

1. Prices established by the producer-seller, which announces from time to time the price at which it is prepared to sell.

2. Prices reported at stated time intervals by a reputable, independent source (frequently a trade periodical) which undertakes to make careful market surveys in order to ascertain actual transaction prices.

3. Prices negotiated directly between seller and buyer. Frequently, but not always, these involve contracts over an extended period. Prices may be subject to adjustment under agreed conditions.

4. Prices established on commodity exchanges, the so-called futures markets. In essence, this is an auction by public outcry, open to any person with appropriate credit standing. Only minerals that have relatively high unit value, that enjoy broad markets, and that are produced to agreed standard specifications are currently traded. However, these minerals account for a large share of the aggregate value of all mineral production.

Given the choice most sellers would opt for method 1. It is still the prevailing mode by which prices of many minerals are established. Over the years market forces have led to the emergence of alternative pricing methods. Thus, problems of conflicting interests that can arise between mines and processing plants have prompted them to resort to independent price arbiters, such as the trade press. Long-term arrangements by which steel plants secure iron ore and other raw materials are usually based on direct price negotiation between buyer and seller. And the development of minerals trading on futures markets primarily reflects two motives — one, the desire of some producers and users to hedge pricing risks and, second, the desire of investor-speculators to realize capital gains if they can correctly anticipate price changes.

For some mineral commodities most transactions are based on a single method. For other commodities two or three of the methods cited may be in active use. And, in a few instances, all four methods may prevail.

Lead may be given as an example. In European markets most lead transactions are based on the price quoted on the London Metal

Exchange (method 4). In Japan most lead sales are at prices established by domestic producers (method 1). In the United States large tonnages are sold at the average lead prices quoted by *Metals Week,* a trade publication (method 2). And imported lead is commonly sold in Latin America at prices negotiated between an importing merchant and the local consumer (method 3).

The four pricing systems do not exist in isolation. Sellers and buyers in most countries are keenly aware of current quotations elsewhere. Any attempt by a seller in one market to maintain a price substantially in excess of other prices will be strongly resisted. The various prices do reflect tariffs and other trade barriers, as well as transportation costs, but at most times they bear a predictable relationship to each other. Canny merchants and traders are prompt to undertake arbitrage should excessive differentials develop.

What are the advantages and disadvantages, the strengths and weaknesses, of each of the pricing methods described? No two observers are likely to be in complete agreement in answering this question. Producers, consumers, commodity traders, government officials, the trade press, the financial community, and university professors each have their views — often heated — on the subject. Individual experiences and prejudices doubtless colour opinions.

Certainly no single method of establishing prices has been developed that will satisfy everyone or be appropriate for every occasion. The descriptions that follow are intended to be objective and factual but some readers may feel that essentials have been omitted or serious deficiences have been ignored.

Producer Pricing

A simple example of the producer pricing method is the asking price for home-made lemonade or iced tea on the part of a nine-year-old seller sitting at a roadside stand. Usually with the active assistance of mother, he or she has produced a limited supply of drinks, offered at a price assumed adequate to dispose of the available supply. If trade is slow, the seller may reduce the price before day's end. If trade is brisk, the seller may close shop and go the nearest brook or pond for a swim; or, if ambitious, a new batch may be produced — the classic response to rising demand. If a neighbouring child sets up in competition, the seller may choose to reduce prices to attract consumers to his stand.

In the minerals industries, producer pricing has been the method initially employed for most commodities. Like the lemonade seller, the minerals marketer in establishing a producer price takes into account his productive capacity, the probable demand, and the presence or absence of competitive sellers. If the seller has control over the entire available supply, the result is monopoly pricing.

Monopolies are rare, however. In the past Greenland cryolite and Chilean nitrate were two instances of apparent monopolies of specific mineral products. In both cases synthetic substitutes were developed and the monopoly power was lost.

More usual are what economists call oligopolies — markets dominated by a few strong sellers. In the years following World War II three minerals that appeared to be controlled by oligopolies were aluminium, nickel and molybdenum. Under strong price leadership by the dominant companies in these industries, prices were maintained at relatively stable levels for a considerable period of time.

During the era of price stability, the world aluminium industry was largely (but not entirely) in the hands of a few major producers. A single producer — Climax in molybdenum and International Nickel in nickel — long accounted for more than half the global output of those two minerals.

The strategy followed in each of these three markets during the era of oligopoly control was to maintain prices that yielded an adequate return to the producers but that were low enough to expand sales volume through penetration of markets previously served by other materials. The strategy was highly successful. Between 1950 and 1973, global aluminium consumption increased at a compound rate of 8% annually. Nickel and molybdenum consumption increased at compound rates of about 6% annually. These gains were markedly greater than the level of growth during the same period enjoyed by competitive materials with less stable prices.

During this era the infrequent changes in the prices of the three metals were primarily related to major cost factors. Alcoa and Alcan in aluminium, Climax in molybdenum, and Inco in nickel acted as the world price leaders. Most world trade in the three metals took place at the prices they established. On occasion smaller producers or merchants quoted discounts from the prices of the leaders in periods of poor business or asked for premiums in periods of soaring demand — but the tonnages changing hands in these grey markets were relatively small.

Eventually, the growth in demand for these materials and their stable price behaviour combined to attract new entrants into the three industries. Prospectors found new deposits of all three. Despite complex technology and high capital costs, rival enterprises were established and the market share of the price leaders dwindled.

The turning point in the commercial structure of all three metals followed the recession of 1975 which had been sparked by the energy crisis. By 1978 the London Metal Exchange initiated trading in aluminium, followed by nickel in 1979. Because molybdenum is primarily sold as concentrate or oxides, it thus far has not been listed for trading due to the difficulty of developing standard specifications essential to futures markets.

Currently prices of aluminium, molybdenum and nickel are exhibiting the volatility long characteristic of other base metals. The post World War II history of the aluminium market clearly illustrates the differences between a market dominated by producer prices and one responding chiefly to commodity exchange trading. This experience will be examined in detail later.

Producer pricing is still the method most widely used for commercial transactions covering two important categories of mineral commodities — non-metallic minerals and the so-called minor metals.

Non-metallic minerals such as sulphur, potash, phosphate rock, barite, gypsum, fluorspar and asbestos share many common characteristics. They are bulk materials of relatively low unit value that incur substantial transportation costs in shipment to market. The number of significant producers is relatively small and the list of buyers is not a long one. Keen competition prevails in all these markets but price changes tend to be infrequent. No substantial pressures have developed to create alternative pricing systems.

Minor metals are characterized by relatively limited volumes and fairly high unit value. Except for antimony and mercury, many of these elements — bismuth, cadmium, cobalt, tellurium and selenium for example — are by-products recovered in the mining and processing of copper, lead, zinc or the precious metals. Consequently their production varies with the operating rates in the major metal industries. At the same time demand for minor metals arises from activity in highly specialized consuming industries. Thus, demand and supply are frequently out of balance, with periods of pronounced shortages. Prices are unpredictable and highly volatile, characteristics that would appear to encourage trading on futures markets — were it not for the limited size of these industries.

Even though copper, lead and zinc are traded on commodity exchanges, some producers of these major base metals have chosen to sell at their own prices. The existence of these dual prices, sometimes referred to as a 'two-price system', has become a source of controversy. At times wide discrepancies have prevailed between the producer and the exchange prices for considerable periods — but the more normal situation is for the two prices to show parallel trends and rough correspondence. Frequently — but not always — the producer prices quoted by individual sellers are identical.

In some quarters the tendency is to assume that if all producer sellers are quoting the same price at the same time for a given commodity, they must have made collusive arrangements. The fact of uniform pricing, however, is a consequence of the differences between basic commodities and manufactured goods. A basic commodity meets defined specifications, so that the goods of one seller are fungible with the goods offered by other sellers. Manufactured products carry brand names and embody difference of style and quality that permit competitive sellers to maintain different price levels.

A minerals seller who endeavours to maintain a price higher than the price quoted by competitors for any considerable time is certain to lose market share. Conversely, a minerals seller who consistently under quotes his competitors will be swamped with demand that will exhaust his available stocks.

In general, therefore, while differences in price among major producer sellers of a given mineral may prevail for brief periods, they eventually disappear. Either the sellers at the lower price raise their quotations or the sellers at the premium price reduce theirs to the level of the competition.

One metal has been in a unique position. This is tin. It has been subject to international commodity agreements during most of the period since World War II. The experience with the effort to control tin prices is described in some detail in Chapter 6.

Independent Price Arbiters

In several markets an important share of minerals transactions is based on prices quoted by independent sources. Frequently these are prices quoted in established mineral industry periodicals which have gained a reputation for skill in gathering market data from both sellers and buyers.

Among the periodicals whose published prices are most frequently used perhaps the three best known are *Metals Week* and *American Metal Market* in the United States and the *Metal Bulletin* in London. However, a number of others also publish price data at regular intervals and buyers and sellers may mutually agree to abide by such quotations.

The publications regularly canvass leading producers, consumers and merchants dealing in individual metals to ascertain actual prices at which transactions have been concluded. Trade press quotations are rarely used to establish the price for spot sales of small quantities. However, they are quite widely employed as the basis for price determination in contracts covering forward deliveries over an extended period.

The tradition of using *Metals Week* quotations for copper, lead and zinc extends back to the turn of the century when they were known as the *E & MJ* prices. All leading U.S. domestic sellers of the three metals furnished the editorial staff once a week with detailed reports of tonnages and prices of sales, broken down on a daily basis. Thus a weighted average price was derived for each business day. These daily prices in turn were used to calculate average prices for each week, month and year.

The *Metals Week* prices have been widely used in the pricing of the metal contained in ores, concentrates, blister, bullion and other raw materials sold by producers or metal merchants to smelters and refiners. The presumption is that the periodical is an impartial arbiter. Thus, the raw material supplier can feel satisfied it is being paid a price representative of the broad market rather than relying on a single entity — the receiving processor — to determine a price unilaterally. *Metals Week* average prices are also frequently used in refined metals contracts extending over periods of time from one month to one year or more. Sometimes a seller will give buyers the option of paying either the seller's price or the *Metals Week* average price, with the choice to be made at the time that the contract is made.

Analogous to trade press prices are several quotations for specific commodities established by entities other than producers. The oldest and perhaps the best known of these is the Handy & Harman daily silver quotation. Handy & Harman, based in New York, is a U.S. refiner and fabricator of silver which acts as a middleman between the producers and the ultimate consumer. Each day, having ascertained the approximate volume of silver contained in its products to be priced on the basis of that day's quotations, Handy solicits from the principal producers bids to supply a matching amount of silver. Its price, announced about noon, represents its appraisal of what it must pay to cover its sales.

This procedure somewhat resembles but is not precisely equivalent to the so-called daily 'fixings' of gold and silver prices in London. In separate meetings each day the leading British bullion dealers assess the two markets. Offers to sell and bids to buy metal are received from all over the world. They are matched to determine a clearing price, which is then announced as the day's official price. Although this procedure might run afoul of the anti-trust laws if followed in the

United States, nevertheless it is accepted without question by buyers and sellers of precious metals in other parts of the globe.

An interesting international example of a price resulting from inter-governmental discussions held under United Nations auspices is the International Tungsten Indicator. For several years discussions were held in Geneva by representatives of the chief tungsten producing and consuming countries regarding the feasibility of an international agreement to stabilize tungsten prices.

Major differences of opinion emerged as to the desirability of such an arrangement but out of these talks emerged an undertaking to establish a better measure of the tungsten price. The quotation is based on actual transactions. Buyers and sellers provide details of the tonnage sold, metal content of the material involved, and the price paid per unit (1%) of tungsten content in U.S. dollars. The price is calculated fortnightly. A similar calculation is made by the *Metal Bulletin,* with occasional significant differences. Thus, in 1982 the ITI price averaged 6·6% higher than the *Bulletin* price whereas, in 1983, they were virtually identical.

Another independent source of price determination for a single mineral is the NUEXCO Exchange Value of uranium, compiled by a company based in Menlo Park, California. It establishes a monthly price for the value of the U_3O_8 content of spot and future sales. It is based on information obtained both from producer-sellers and from utilities buying fuel for their reactors. Originally established prior to the energy crisis of 1974, it recorded the dramatic change from a buyers' to a sellers' market that occurred in 1973 and then the reversion to a buyers' market as environmental and health concerns thwarted earlier plans to expand nuclear power plant capacities.

Negotiated Prices

Direct negotiations between seller and buyer is, of course, the way prices are agreed in the soukhs and bazaars of the East. Direct negotiations also set prices in certain areas of mineral commerce.

Most common is the use of direct negotiations to determine prices for raw materials required in processing steel and aluminium. These major industries use enormous tonnages of ores, fluxes and fuels. Their operations are geared to handling specific types of feed, the supply of which must be assured for years — if not decades. The miners of iron ore, bauxite, manganese and other minerals used in steel and aluminium production also seek the assurance of a certain outlet for their products which typically must be transported over long distances by bulk carriers.

In these transactions, therefore, the parties have a common interest in an enduring relationship at prices that are acceptable to both. Given the factors of inflation and fluctuating currency values, however, long-term contracts usually contain escalator clauses to modify prices in the event of major cost changes. The quantity of raw material sold may also vary, depending on the state of the market for the finished metal — but as a rule the buyer must provide advance notifications of changes to the seller in order to enable him to alter his shipping arrangements.

Contracts of this nature, often made for periods of five to ten years, played an important role in the development of the Australian and Brazilian iron ore industries and the Jamaican, Australian and Guinean bauxite industries, cited in Chapter 2 as examples of major new mineral sources developed since World War II. The contracts not only provided the miners with assurance of sales outlets at known prices but they greatly facilitated raising the funds needed for mine development and plant construction.

Direct negotiations between sellers and buyers also determine prices in many spot minerals transactions in smaller markets — such as Latin America and southeast Asia. In these deals prices prevailing in other larger markets are adjusted to cover freight and insurance costs, local import duties or other taxes, and other variables. Because these variables are constantly changing, the room for give and take between the parties is considerable.

Commodity Exchange Pricing

In the minds of the lay public, not directly involved in the minerals industry, a reference to prices for most of the major non-ferrous metals inevitably conjures up the prices quoted on the commodity exchanges. Gold and silver are traded on many different exchanges around the world but for the base metals the significant markets are the London Metal Exchange and the New York Commodity Exchange. Recently Kuala Lumpur has opened an important market in tin.

The commodity exchanges provide a mechanism by which a seller can sell or a buyer can buy at a price determined by public outcry for delivery at a stated time. A contract, once made, must be performed either by delivery of the commodity sold or by an offsetting transaction — that is, a seller may meet his obligation to make delivery by resale. The principal exception to performance is government fiat — on outbreak of war exchanges have at times been closed. On such occasions the ruling board of the exchange decides in what manner and on what terms outstanding commitments must be liquidated.

For many years most of the commodities traded on exchanges were agricultural products such as wheat, corn, cotton, sugar, coffee, eggs, pork bellies, and soy beans. Characteristically for agricultural commodities there are thousands of producer-sellers and consumer-buyers.

Demand for agricultural commodities tends to be fairly constant, varying with population trends but relatively unaffected by the business cycle. On the other hand, the supply of agricultural commodities may be seriously influenced by unpredictable events — notably the weather. Thus these commodities have elastic supply and relatively inelastic demand — the reverse of the situation that prevails with minerals. From the standpoint of the speculator, the supply-demand relationship for a farm crop hinges on a factor difficult to forecast — the weather. Thus, at any given time, speculative opinion as to agricultural prices tends to be fairly evenly divided.

The industrial commodities, particularly the metals, are in a very different category. The variable factors are closely related to the business cycle. In periods of recession speculators in industrial commodities turn bearish. In periods of recovery the great majority will assume a bullish posture. This means that the producer who wishes to use the commodity exchange as a hedging mechanism will find that if he wants to sell forward to assure himself of sales during a period of business decline, the effects of sales on an exchange is to depress prices further; while in a time of increasing business activity, the consumer, anxious to assure himself of supplies, will find that forward purchases on an exchange will tend to push prices upward.

Rightly or wrongly, most metal producers and many metal consumers have come to believe that the existence of the futures markets has tended to increase price instability for the metals traded on them. They recognize that these markets provide certain advantages — for instance, the opportunity to hedge price risks and the assurance that sellers can always dispose of product or buyers can always obtain a wanted commodity. Yet there is a feeling that those advantages are more than counterbalanced by the boom-or-bust fluctuations in price that have characterized these markets since 1970.

The succeeding chapter examines developments in the aluminium, copper and silver markets in the turbulent years since 1970 in an effort to delineate how the futures markets have functioned.

CHAPTER FIVE

Trading in Minerals on the Commodity Exchanges

Mechanics of Futures Trading

Trading on commodity exchanges has a pronounced impact on commodity price behaviour. To gain insight into this one must understand the mechanics of exchange trading — how it differs from other commercial transactions.

A commodity exchange is in essence an auction, conducted during prescribed hours of each business day. Anyone with an appropriate credit rating may participate, utilizing the services of a member of the particular exchange. Trading is not limited to producers, users and dealers in the commodity.

As mentioned in the previous chapter, the two principal commodity exchanges which trade futures in minerals are the London Metal Exchange (LME) and the New York Commodity Exchange (COMEX). LME is the older of these two institutions. It is viewed by most as being primarily a market where producers, consumers, scrap merchants and metal dealers may hedge their price risks. Although COMEX is also used for hedging purposes, many consider it to be primarily a vehicle for speculators seeking to realize gains by correctly anticipating changes in commodity prices.

The two exchanges differ in significant ways. To cite just a few: the maximum time period for trading, the margin requirements, the size of the individual contract units, and the methods of settling contracts are all different.

LME commodities are traded for the prompt or 'cash' position, requiring immediate delivery, and for future delivery, at any agreed date, up to 90 days forward. Silver is an exception in that trading covers a maximum forward period of seven months. COMEX contracts specify the month of delivery, including the current month, and future months up to a maximum of 22 months forward.

Until the tin crisis, the LME had no formal margin requirements, again except for trading in silver. Each ring-dealing member determined what margin he would require his clients to deposit when trading. On COMEX margin requirements are established by the Exchange board of governors. They are rigidly enforced for all traders.

COMEX contracts have always cleared through a central clearing organization. In the past LME contracts have been settled directly between members of the Exchange. The events following suspension of tin trading in late 1985, however, have caused reconsideration of this practice and steps are now being considered by the LME to institute a central clearing arrangement.

Both exchanges establish the size of the individual contract, the specifications of quality constituting acceptable delivery, and the brand names of the producers which may be traded. These decisions are made by the governing boards. On both exchanges, the seller has the option to deliver goods to the warehouse of his choice. Normally he will choose the one involving the least cost of delivery. On both exchanges warehouses approved for delivery are located in numerous geographical locations — principal European and British ports in the case of the LME and cities widely distributed throughout the U.S. in the case of COMEX.

The buyer is obliged to accept the warehouse certificate tendered to him at the time the contract matures. Any brand approved by the exchange constitutes good delivery. Thus, the buyer faces the possibility of receiving an unfamiliar brand at an inconvenient location. To overcome these problems, a buyer may arrange a swap or exchange through the member firm he has used as his broker — but at times this will involve an additional payment to ensure that he secures a known brand at an appropriate warehouse.

The size of the contract unit may vary as between the exchanges. For example, LME copper contracts are for 25 metric tons. This conforms to industry practice, since most refineries weigh and assay their production in standard 25-ton lots. COMEX copper contracts are for 25,000 pounds (12½ short tons). This obliges producers who make deliveries to COMEX warehouses to provide additional records of weights and analysis. COMEX adopted this deviation from trade practice to encourage trading by individuals. Margin requirements for the smaller contract of 25,000 pounds are set at a lesser amount than prevailed for a lot of 50,000 pounds, the previous contract size.

One aspect of futures market trading that puzzles the general public is the distinction between physical transactions and paper transactions. Only a small proportion of the contracts traded result in actual delivery of the commodity traded. In most cases, the seller of a commodity for future delivery has no intention of delivering to an exchange warehouse. He sells to establish the price he will receive at a future date. Before the date stipulated for delivery, he expects to buy back on the exchange what he has earlier sold. The buyer, the party on the other end of the transaction, also usually does not intend to take delivery when he buys futures. Prior to the date when the contract matures, he expects to sell back to the market the metal he has originally bought.

Motives for Entering into Exchange Contracts
If there is no intention to deliver or receive physical material, why enter into a transaction? Basically there are three motives — hedging, speculation or earning a secure return on idle cash.

A producer sells on an exchange to establish a known price for his future output. When ready to ship from his plant, he prefers to deliver to one of his established customers — consumers with whom he has continuing relations.

Similarly, the consumer buys on the exchange in order to establish a known cost for raw materials he will need in the future. Rather than take delivery from an exchange warehouse of material with which he is unfamiliar (even though it meets specifications), he sells on the exchange what he had earlier bought and arranges to receive his requirements from his regular supplier.

Typical of hedging transactions on commodity exchanges are those entered into by custom smelters, the processing plants that buy raw materials from mines or scrap dealers and that sell refined metal to fabricators and manufacturers. A price risk exists between the time purchased material arrives at the smelter and the time refined metal is available for delivery. To cover this risk, the custom smelter makes a forward sale on the exchange of an amount of metal equal to the recoverable content of the raw material he has bought. Later, when he is in a position to deliver physical metal, the seller seeks out a customer who will pay the then prevailing price. As an offset he simultaneously buys back the metal previously sold on the commodity exchange.

Indeed, it was the need of custom smelters in the nineteenth century to protect themselves against price changes between the time they bought raw materials and the time they were in a position to deliver refined metal that is given as the explanation for the founding of the London Metal Exchange.

The price the seller pays to buy back his earlier sale or the buyer receives when he sells back his original purchase is likely to differ from the original transaction price. This will result either in a profit or a loss on the exchange trade. But there will be an offsetting loss or gain in the direct commercial transaction. Thus, except for the cost of commissions, the hedger operating on an exchange has in effect bought or sold at the price of the original transaction, established prior to the time when the metal becomes physically available.

Those who trade on exchanges for speculative purposes do so because they have an opinion as to the probable price trend. They buy and sell commodities much as the speculator in securities buys and sells stocks and bonds. Their motives are simply to buy cheap and sell dear. If they believe the price of a commodity is likely to rise, they will buy first and sell later. If they believe the price is likely to fall, they will sell short first and buy back later.

In addition to hedgers and speculators, a third group of traders are those who buy spot metal for immediate delivery, provided they can make corresponding sales for later delivery at a higher price. These traders are looking for a secure return on the cash they put up.

If adequate stocks of the commodity traded are in the exchange warehouses, prices quoted for future delivery are normally higher than prices quoted for spot delivery. This spread is called a 'contango' and under typical circumstances it will be roughly equal to the prevailing interest rate paid on low-risk short-term investments. Since commodity futures contracts are not subject to *force majeure,* a conservative investor who owns commodities in an exchange warehouse can feel confident that his offsetting future sale will be performed. In effect, traders who buy spot and sell forward at the contango spread are carrying inventories not wanted by others. This becomes of significant importance in times of general surplus.

When inventories in the exchange warehouses begin to diminish, the contango normally narrows. If inventories drop to a very low level or if they are held by a well-financed owner who does not sell forward, the contango may disappear entirely. When the spot price is at a premium over the futures price, the spread is called a 'backwardation'. This can make an awkward situation for the speculator who has sold short and must buy back because he has no physical material to deliver when his contract matures.

Backwardations are relatively rare. The more usual situation is for the contango, or premium for futures, to equal the carrying cost (interest and warehouse charges) of the money tied up in the inventories.

Relatively small amounts of metal are normally moved into exchange warehouses. Most mineral production is shipped directly by producers to users as a consequence of direct commercial transactions — which, in many cases, are negotiated at the prices prevailing on the exchanges.

When metal is physically delivered to exchange warehouses, documents are issued evidencing that the material has been received. One certificate is provided for each contract unit. Thus, for example, if a copper producer delivers 200 tons, an LME warehouseman will issue eight certificates covering eight contract units of 25 tons each.

The option of delivering to an exchange warehouse is of value to a producer whose sales have lagged behind his projections and who needs immediate cash. It is also attractive to sellers who do not wish to go to the expense of creating sales and marketing organizations to handle a relatively limited production. The centrally-planned countries, in particular, have found the LME a convenient way to dispose of their exports as a means of securing hard currency.

Consumers always have the option of taking delivery from exchange warehouses if they can buy at prices lower than those being quoted by producers. Because of this, producers in turn usually find it desirable to maintain their prices close to the level of the quotations prevailing on the exchanges.

This need to parallel exchange price trends makes it difficult for producers to offset cost increases by raising prices. As an example, traders in futures consider that a wage settlement, no matter how costly, reduces the threat of shortage. They lower their bids, therefore, at the very time when production costs are increasing and producers wish to increase revenues.

To illustrate how futures trading can affect the price behaviour of individual commodities, two examples are cited. One is the way in which the pattern of aluminium pricing has changed since the inception of futures trading of that commodity. The other is the remarkable events of 1979-80 in the precious metals markets.

The Contrast Between Aluminium and Copper

Until very recent years, prices of aluminium have behaved very differently from prices of copper. These metals are the two largest non-ferrous metal industries in amounts and values of global output. They are alike in many ways. Both are extractive, non-renewable materials. They compete with each other in many markets — generation and distribution of electric energy, construction, transportation, and all types of machinery.

Copper prices have traditionally been erratic performers. As an example, the price of copper on the London Metal Exchange rose from a low of £446 a ton (metric) in January 1973 to a high of £1,400 a ton in April 1974, only to fall back by the end of 1974 to £529 a ton. Thus, within a two-year span, the price varied by more than 300%.

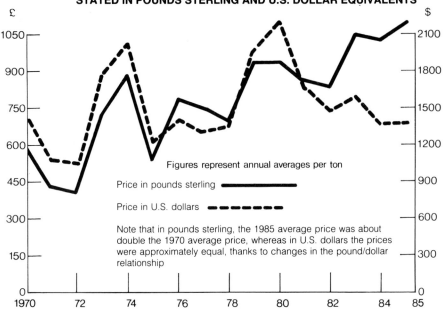

CHART   4. LONDON METAL EXCHANGE PRICES FOR COPPER 1970-85
STATED IN POUNDS STERLING AND U.S. DOLLAR EQUIVALENTS

Figures represent annual averages per ton

Price in pounds sterling ▬▬▬▬▬

Price in U.S. dollars ▬ ▬ ▬ ▬ ▬

Note that in pounds sterling, the 1985 average price was about
double the 1970 average price, whereas in U.S. dollars the prices
were approximately equal, thanks to changes in the pound/dollar
relationship

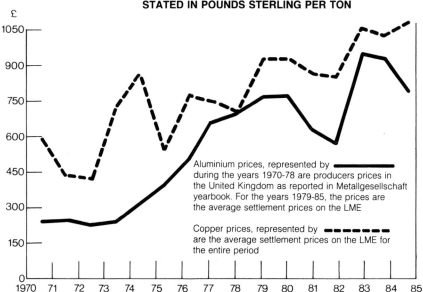

CHART   5. AVERAGE PRICES FOR ALUMINIUM AND COPPER 1970-85
STATED IN POUNDS STERLING PER TON

Aluminium prices, represented by ▬▬▬▬
during the years 1970-78 are producers prices in
the United Kingdom as reported in Metallgesellschaft
yearbook. For the years 1979-85, the prices are
the average settlement prices on the LME

Copper prices, represented by ▬ ▬ ▬ ▬ ▬
are the average settlement prices on the LME for
the entire period

96

By contrast, aluminium prices were the epitome of stability until the mid-seventies. The price at times remained unchanged for as long as two years. Three changes within one year were considered unusual.

The disparity in price behaviour redounded to aluminium's benefit and to copper's detriment. If both metals were suitable for a given application, a manufacturer tended to use aluminium rather than copper because he could better anticipate his raw-material costs. Performance characteristics were important but when the evidence indicated both metals were satisfactory, the choice was likely to be aluminium rather than copper. In the era of economic expansion following World War II, global aluminium consumption grew at a compound rate of 8%, double the 4% rate experienced by copper.

Repeatedly, copper sellers were asked by customers, annoyed by extreme price swings, why they could not emulate aluminium's example.

It seemed a relevant question — something like the plaintive complaint by Professor Higgins in the musical comedy, *My Fair Lady,* when he asked, "Why can't a woman be more like a man?" The answer to the question about copper and aluminium prices — as about the sexes — was both complex and fundamental.

In part the differing price behaviour between the two elements is due to the structure of the industries. Aluminium is an abundant element, with ample ore supplies. In the market-economy countries it is produced from bauxite, of which there are numerous high-grade deposits. Thus, raw-material costs for aluminium production are fairly uniform among producers. By contrast, copper ores are relatively scarce and have much lower metal contents than bauxite. Substantial differences in grade and costs exist among the major deposits. As a consequence, the ability to find and develop low-cost ore deposits is the key to success in copper. This is risky, time-consuming and capital intensive.

For years the supply of electric energy, the largest factor in aluminium costs, was plentiful and its price was predictable. Copper's price instability was partially the consequence of the large share of copper supplies originating in developing countries with turbulent

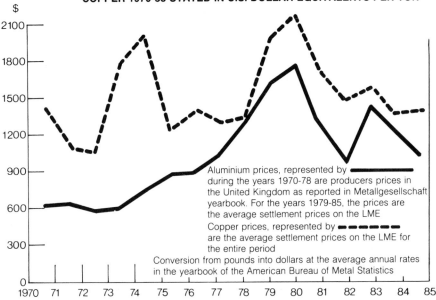

CHART 6. AVERAGE UNITED KINGDOM PRICES FOR ALUMINIUM AND COPPER 1970-85 STATED IN U.S. DOLLAR EQUIVALENTS PER TON

Aluminium prices, represented by ▬▬▬▬
during the years 1970-78 are producers prices in
the United Kingdom as reported in Metallgesellschaft
yearbook. For the years 1979-85, the prices are
the average settlement prices on the LME

Copper prices, represented by ▬ ▬ ▬ ▬ ▬
are the average settlement prices on the LME for
the entire period

Conversion from pounds into dollars at the average annual rates
in the yearbook of the American Bureau of Metal Statistics

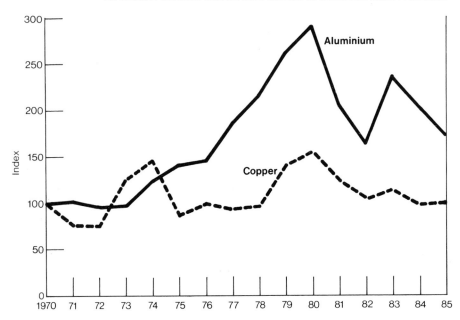

CHART 7. AVERAGE PRICES FOR ALUMINIUM AND COPPER
1970-85
INDEXED ON BASIS OF 1970 PRICES EQUALLING 100
AVERAGE UNITED KINGDOM PRICES IN DOLLAR EQUIVALENTS

political problems. Furthermore, copper production from industrialized countries was often subject to prolonged disputes between labour and management, whereas aluminium producers had a record of stable industrial relations.

Price Behaviour in the Years since 1970

Equally important was another factor. Copper was traded on futures markets. Before 1979 aluminium was not traded on those markets. This was an important difference and can be illustrated by examining the course of prices for the two metals during the years since 1970. This period breaks down into three distinct phases:

The years 1970-73 were typical of the post-war expansionist era, with moderate cyclical changes in the world economy.

The years 1974-78 saw drastic changes, notably the energy crisis induced by the tripling of oil prices in 1974, followed by a severe recession and then gradual recovery as world trade adjusted to the new circumstances.

The years 1979-85 started with a second round of sharply rising oil prices, again followed by a severe recession and then once again gradual recovery.

For aluminium the years 1979-85 were very different from the years 1970-73 and 1974-78. To a major extent this was the consequence of the inception of trading in aluminium on the futures markets in 1978. The subsequent course of events provides a striking demonstration of what happens when an industry, long dominated by producer established prices, must suddenly cope with trading of its output on the futures markets.

The average prices of aluminium and copper in the United Kingdom in each year since 1970 are shown in Charts 5 and 6. Because of fluctuations in foreign exchange values during these difficult years they are expressed both in pounds sterling and in dollars. Although no single market can be completely representative, U.K. prices are generally accepted as the most indicative of international trends. The United States is the largest consumer of non-ferrous metals but prices there have at times been subject to government-dictated price ceilings. At other times they have been heavily influenced by largely domestic considerations (although, of course, always subject to international developments).

During the years 1970-73 the aluminium industry enjoyed dynamic market expansion and stable prices, as had been the case since 1950. Substantial additions were made to plant capacity to meet soaring demand. Although consumption levelled off in 1971, only modest price unsettlement developed. Some metal was offered by merchants at modest discounts from producer prices but the quantities involved represented only a minor share of the total market. As the dollar/pound relationship remained relatively steady, price trends were similar regardless of the currency in which they were expressed.

Copper had a more difficult time during 1970-73. In the sixties an effort by some producers to stabilize prices had failed and in the later years of the decade prices had risen to record levels, exacerbated by a lengthy strike at U.S. mines in 1967-68. As a consequence, a plethora of new copper projects was launched. Despite increasing consumption, significant over-capacity resulted. Thus, the mild recession of 1971 brought about a pronounced weakening of copper prices that persisted into 1972.

However, 1973 proved to be a different story. Copper consumption rose sharply to establish new records. The 1972 report of the Club of Rome induced consumer fears of eventual shortage. Buyers noted that Chilean production had sagged under the leftist régime in power when the year began. As copper prices started to climb in London, trade patterns became distorted because the price ceilings effective in the United States induced exports of scrap supplies and some refined metal. The 1973 average London copper price, whether stated in pounds sterling or in dollars, exceeded the 1972 price by about 70%.

The second phase — the years 1974-78 — marked the development of the energy crisis. For aluminium it was a period of steady and substantial price advances, regardless of the phase of the business cycle. Thus, even though consumption of aluminium in 1975 was markedly below consumption in 1974 (see Chart 2, p. 20), the price of aluminium was increased that year. The rationale on the part of the producers in raising prices was clear — energy and labour costs were rising sharply. In addition, several bauxite exporting countries had increased export taxes, adding to raw material costs.

In spite of diminished sales in 1975, aluminium prices rose. To avoid accumulating excessive inventories and tying up available cash (or borrowing from banks at rising interest costs), aluminium output was temporarily curtailed. By 1976 signs of recovery were on hand; production was increased as demand improved and the industry was able to advance prices again to offset rampant inflation. This formula was repeated in 1977 and again in 1978. Industry profit margins were well maintained and the tonnages of metal sold exceeded the previous record levels of 1973 and 1974. During this period, the value of the pound in terms of dollars was substantially less than it had been in 1970-73. Hence, the price in dollars did not rise quite as steeply as the price in pounds sterling.

Copper prices tell a very different story in the 1974-78 period. Although the copper industry was also subject to sharply rising costs, it was unable to offset them with higher revenues. True, the first of the five years, 1974, had been marked by a substantial rise in price over the 1973 average. This rise occurred entirely in the first half of the year, during the speculative frenzy that followed the tripling of oil prices. Indeed, the press published articles speculating that copper exporters, through their organization, CIPEC, would emulate the example of OPEC and establish a marketing cartel.

This expectation proved short-lived. By mid-year 1974 the drastic change in world trade and balance of payments difficulties resulting from higher oil prices created world-wide recession. As sales of manufactured products dwindled, industry decided to reduce excess raw material inventories. Buying virtually ceased. Prices of those commodities traded on futures exchanges began a sharp descent — with copper particularly hard hit.

During 1975 some curtailment of production took place in the United States and Canada. Other copper producers, notably in Third World countries, however, continued to operate at effective capacity (there was a brief unsuccessful effort by CIPEC members to institute cut-backs, more honoured in the breach than in the observance). The public sector companies chose to maintain full employment and earn foreign exchange by maximizing exports — thus assisting their governments to cover interest on foreign debt and to pay for needed imports. In essence, this policy was directly contrary to that then followed by OPEC — which restricted production to maximize price. The fact that surplus copper output could be sold on the commodity exchanges was undoubtedly a major consideration for these copper producers — even if rising stocks in exchange warehouses drove prices downward.

Although copper consumption shared in the industrial recovery of 1976-78, commodity exchange warehouse stocks continued to mount as production remained high. It should be noted that dollar copper prices remained at or below the 1970 level throughout 1975-78. Sterling prices were higher than in the 1970 base year only because of the sharp decline in the pound sterling's value in relation to dollars.

Thus, the copper price, determined primarily by traders on the futures markets, reflected their perceptions of the supply/demand balance in the copper industry. These perceptions did not take into account the effects of inflation on copper production costs — even though one might argue that in the long run costs must eventually affect supply and hence price.

On the other hand, during the years 1974-78 the aluminium price was established by the producers — independent of any judgements held by dealers or speculators. The producers were primarily motivated by cost factors in making price decisions. Without the opportunity to sell surplus inventories for cash, on a commodity exchange, aluminium producers had adjusted output rates to the level of actual consumption. This avoided a build-up of excess stocks and facilitated further price increases to offset rising costs.

Aluminium Trading Starts
During 1978 the board of the London Metal Exchange asked leading aluminium producers whether they favoured the introduction of trading in aluminium futures. Fully cognizant of the advantages aluminium had enjoyed in competition with copper in the past,

thanks to stable aluminium prices and volatile copper prices — and particularly aware of the melancholy profits record of the copper industry during 1975-77 — the major aluminium firms responded that they saw no advantage in having the metal traded on a futures market. Further, they commented that they perceived no real need for such a facility since they had always supplied whatever metal was required by industry.

In spite of this negative response, the LME board decided to proceed. They believed — correctly as it turned out — that sufficient quantities of aluminium to make aluminium trading viable could be attracted from public sector producers in the developing world and from producers in the centrally-planned countries. After a slow start in late 1978, the volume of trading gradually developed. By 1980 the market was in full swing.

Prices for the years 1979-85 reveal how the aluminium market has been affected by futures trading. In 1979 prices rose as recovery continued and double-digit inflation prevailed in many industrialized countries. Prices in pounds sterling remained strong in 1980. The dollar price showed a substantial gain, reflecting the decline in the dollar's value relative to the pound sterling that year.

In 1981 a new recession began, widely attributed to the fresh round of oil price increases initiated in late 1979. For the first time since 1974 aluminium prices declined. The decline accelerated in 1982 when aluminium sales fell sharply. Inventories reported by producers and in LME warehouses increased as new production came on-stream, notably from developing world producers.

In contrast with previous experience, aluminium prices in 1982 softened to a greater extent than copper prices. The 1982 aluminium prices, both in pounds sterling and in dollars, were lower than in 1978 whereas 1982 copper prices were modestly above the corresponding 1978 figures.

Industrial recovery began in 1983 and aluminium prices quickly responded, while copper lagged behind. Indeed, for a short time in late 1983 and early 1984, aluminium prices in both pounds sterling and dollars were higher than copper prices — a relationship that had not existed since shortly after the end of World War II. But by

103

mid-1984 it became clear that aluminium stocks were again rising. Despite some modest reductions in production rates by North American producers, increases elsewhere were more than enough to offset the cut-backs. Prices of both metals were weak on the futures markets, but aluminium prices were distinctly weaker than copper prices. Both were so low as to cause great distress for most producers.

The picture of long-term relationships in the prices of the two metals that emerges from these events appears to warrant these conclusions:

1. The energy crisis and subsequent inflation pushed aluminium prices sharply higher between 1974 and 1979.

2. At the same time, copper prices remained low, even though inflation had also had a substantial, if lesser, impact on copper production costs.

3. Thus, the wide spread between aluminium and copper prices that had prevailed since the mid-fifties was perceptibly narrowed. This tended to improve copper's position to a certain extent in some competitive markets.

4. In the past, copper producers have been urged to take steps to make their prices less volatile in the hope that this would promote market growth such as had been long enjoyed by the aluminium industry, thanks to a relatively stable pattern of prices.

5. Once aluminium trading began on commodity exchanges, however, aluminium prices also became volatile. Rather than copper emulating aluminium, aluminium prices appear now to be following the pattern that has long prevailed for copper prices.

6. Exchange trading has undoubtedly played a large role in this. A second major contributing factor has been the increasing share of world aluminium production accounted for by developing countries. In 1968 Europe, the United States, Canada and Japan accounted for 92·2% of aluminium production among market-economy countries. By 1984 their share of global output had declined to 73·7% of a much larger total — indeed, the volume had about doubled. With abundant energy sources available in some developing countries and with energy costs in the industrialized countries rising sharply (except perhaps in Australia and Canada), the proportion of aluminium

output originating in developing countries seems certain to continue growing.

The Role of the Speculator

How important a role in futures market price trends is played by outright speculation as compared with hedging?

The classic theory is that speculators help to stabilize markets by purchasing commodities when demand slumps and by selling when demand revives. Long observation of the mineral markets appears to warrant the opposite conclusion. Speculative buying interest is greatest when concrete evidence develops that an economic upturn is in the making, with expectations of a revival in industrial purchasing. In periods of economic downturn, speculators are disinclined to buy industrial commodities. They wait for positive signs of recovery before re-entering the market.

It is true that in slumps, institutions or persons with idle cash may be willing to buy prompt metal provided they can simultaneously sell forward at a sufficient premium or contango to yield them a return comparable with what they can secure in other directions. However, since they are taking a hedged position and are not in a true sense net buyers, their operations have no real influence on price trends.

The magnitude of speculative operations on the exchanges can be indicated by examining the figures for trading in copper, gold and silver on COMEX. In each year since 1976 more than one million copper contracts have been traded on COMEX. In 1984 a new high mark was reached — over 2·5 million contracts — equivalent to 30 million short tons of copper. This is 15 times the level of United States' annual consumption and more than three times the level of world consumption of the metal. Obviously no such volume of trading is needed simply to hedge price risks on the part of trade interests.

Why has speculation in commodities become so active? The answer appears to lie in the low margin requirements. The amount of margin a buyer or seller is required to post on COMEX is fixed by its board of governors and typically is between 5% and 10% of the value of the contract based on prevailing prices. This contrasts with margin requirements of 50% or more on security transactions. For their more aggressive clients, brokerage firms have been quick to point out the greater leverage obtained with a given amount of funds if commodities are traded rather than securities.

Assuming the price of copper is likely to rise, a bigger profit will result from posting $10,000 as margin to purchase COMEX copper contracts than the same amount of margin used to buy securities of a copper producing firm. While the risk of loss is also greater in commodity trading should copper prices decline rather than increase, the prospect of quick profits obviously has attracted many followers. Large as the volume of copper trading on COMEX may seem in relation to the size of the industry, it is modest in comparison with the volume of trading in gold and silver on that exchange.

Even though gold is traded on many other exchanges throughout the world, the trading in gold on COMEX alone has averaged over 10 million contracts annually. Since each contract represents 100 ounces, this means that one billion ounces of gold annually — worth hundreds of billions of dollars — is traded on the floor of that single exchange. World gold production has been approximately 40 million ounces a year, so COMEX trading alone is 25 times current annual gold production.

The volume of silver trading on COMEX has been erratic in recent years, varying between a low of 1,058,734 contracts in 1980 and a high of 6,742,508 contracts in 1984 — with the average somewhat over three million contracts. The contract unit is 5,000 ounces. Hence the average trading volume is equivalent to 15,000 million ounces or 50 times the annual volume of new silver mine production. Like gold, silver is also traded on several other United States' exchanges besides COMEX.

Clearly for these two metals, futures trading is primarily related to speculation rather than hedging. Indeed, advertisements in the financial press and on television are constantly informing the public of purported profit opportunities in these two commodities.

Perhaps no single price phenomenon of recent times, other than the OPEC actions on crude oil, has attracted more public interest than the remarkable events in the gold and silver markets during 1979 and 1980.

The Special Role of Gold and Silver

These events followed dramatic changes in the role gold and silver had long played in mankind's monetary arrangements. Gold and silver are unique commodities; since the earliest days of civilization they have been seen as synonymous with money. Indeed, the French and Spanish words for money and for silver are the same — argent in French, plata in Spanish.

Consider the first reference to money in the Bible. This occurs in Genesis, which describes Abraham's purchase of a burial plot for his wife, Sarah, by payment of "four hundred shekels of silver, current money with the merchant". Similar examples of mankind's high regard for both metals can be found throughout the records of ancient times in many lands.

Of the two metals, over the centuries, gold was more widely used as the reserve basis for currencies, while silver coins became the standard for daily trade in the market place. As international commerce developed, principal trading nations based their monetary systems on a fixed price for gold — the gold standard. These governments were prepared to buy any gold offered at that standard price and to sell, when bid, at the same price. Trade balances between nations were settled by shifting gold reserves from one central bank to another.

The British pound, which long prevailed as the principal currency for international trade, was based on a gold price of 84½ shillings an ounce — a value set by Sir Isaac Newton as Master of the Royal Mint in 1703. The United States' official price was later set at $20·67 an ounce, which corresponded to the British price on the basis of a parity with the pound at $4·86.

The First World War, followed by the great Depression of the thirties, forced both the United Kingdom and the United States to abandon the gold standard — as did all the other major trading nations. Paper currencies were no longer redeemable in gold.

107

However, central banks continued the use of gold as an important reserve asset. In 1934, the United States fixed the price of gold at $35 an ounce. Under regulations issued then, it was prepared to buy gold at that price from all sellers but would only sell gold either to central banks in settlement of international balances or to licensed industrial users of gold (including the jewellery trade) in carefully controlled amounts. Individuals or corporations not having licences were forbidden to own gold bullion or gold coins (except for numismatic purposes).

Many other countries followed the United States' pattern. The $35 price attracted a steady flow of gold to the United States. By the

TABLE 6: CROWN SIZE SILVER COINS AS MINTED IN 1900

Country	Coin Denomination	Weight (g)	Fineness*	Silver Content (oz)
Great Britain	Crown (5 shillings)	28·276	925	0·8409
United States	Dollar	26·730	900	0·7734
Argentina	Peso	25·000	900	0·7234
Austria	5 Kronen	24·000	900	0·6944
Austria (export)	Thaler	28·067	833	0·7520
Belgium	5 Francs	25·000	900	0·7234
Brazil	2000 Reis	25·500	917	0·7515
Egypt	20 Ghirsh	28·000	833	0·7502
Ethiopia	1 Ber	28·075	835	0·7537
France	5 Francs	25·000	900	0·7234
German States	5 Marks	27·777	900	0·8038
Iran	500 Dinar	23·025	900	0·6620
Italy	5 Lire	25·000	900	0·7234
Japan	1 Yen	26·957	900	0·7800
Mexico	1 Peso	27·073	903	0·7857
Morocco	10 Dirhem	29·116	900	0·8425
Netherlands	2½ Gulden	25·000	945	0·7595
Peru	1 Sol	25·000	900	0·7234
Portugal	1000 Reis	25·000	917	0·7368
Spain	1 Peseta	25·000	900	0·7234
Switzerland	5 Francs	25·000	900	0·7234
Turkey	20 Kurus	24·055	830	0·6419

* Fineness denotes parts of silver per 1000. Balance of weight usually copper. In 1900 China, India and Russia were not minting crown size coins but were issuing smaller coins with silver in a range of 900 to 917 fineness.

Source: *Modern World Coins,* R. S. Yeoman.

108

outbreak of World War II it held well over half of all the world's monetary reserves. Thus, under the Bretton Woods agreement establishing the International Monetary Fund at war's end, national central banks could hold reserves either as U.S. dollars or as gold on the basis of $35 an ounce. This arrangement prevailed until August 1971, when 40 years of inflation had made the $35 peg unrealistic. Then, faced with inflationary trends, adverse trade balances, and declining gold reserves, President Nixon suspended the dollar's convertibility into gold for settling international accounts with other Central Banks. This set the stage for the current era of floating currency exchange rates and fluctuating gold prices.

Silver's role in monetary affairs has been more limited. Few nations have attempted to maintain currencies backed by a silver standard. However, because silver's lesser value made it more compatible with day-to-day over-the-counter trade, silver coinage became the workhorse of currency systems. The standard of coinage became the denominations issued in sizes corresponding to the British crown — five shillings. This coin, minted in the sterling alloy of 925 parts silver and 75 parts copper, set a pattern followed in most other countries. Table 6 lists the crown size coins in circulation in more than a score of nations at the turn of the century. Roughly equivalent in silver content, these coins traded at approximate parity prior to World War I — an era of stable exchange rates.

World War I brought drastic changes. Staggering under the huge costs of war, many belligerent governments resorted to the printing presses. With colossal amounts of paper currency outstanding, silver coins disappeared from circulation in many nations. After the war most governments either reduced or entirely eliminated the silver content of their coins. The United States, Canada and Switzerland were among the few to maintain silver coinage of unchanged weight and fineness.

Indeed, the standard for United States' coinage dated back to 1792 when Alexander Hamilton established the silver content of the dollar at 0·77 ounces. This gave silver a coinage value of $1·29 an ounce. However, silver was not monetized. Market prices for the most part remained well below the coinage value. Government mints realized substantial seignorage profits in issuing silver coins with face values greater than the market value of the contained metal.

Industrial use of silver increased rapidly in the post-World War II period. Global mine production remained relatively static. A gap developed in the supply/demand balance that was met by the disposal of silver stocks accumulated by the U.S. Treasury as a consequence of the legislation enacted in 1934.

Noting the steady diminution in government stocks, speculators began to hoard silver coins, expecting the silver price eventually to rise above its monetary value. U.S. Treasury officials, responsible for ensuring an adequate supply of coins to facilitate trade, were concerned. In 1964 they decided to replace silver coins with a silverless copper-nickel alloy and Switzerland, Canada and other countries followed suit. It took three years to mint enough new coinage to ensure an adequate supply. During these years the Treasury sold most of its remaining stocks to prevent the price rising above the $1·29 monetary value.

By 1967, an adequate supply of new silverless coins was available. Government sales ceased. For the first time in modern history, silver sold at a premium over its U.S. monetary value.

Thus, irresponsible government financing and ensuing inflation had broken the links between the monetary systems of the market-economy world and the two precious metals. A tradition as old as civilization had ended.

In this situation, some economists predicted that prices for both metals would fall. They considered that gold and silver had become simple commodities. They did not believe in the widely held notion that these metals had 'intrinsic value'. Rather, they labelled this concept a 'barbarous relic'. They reasoned that surpluses of both metals would develop because industrial consumption was lower than current new production together with supplies that would be recovered from melting coins. They were confident that these surpluses would demonstrate the fallacy of the belief in the intrinsic value of precious metals.

Thus far, however, their views have been confounded by events. The vast majority of people, conditioned by centuries of tradition, continue to believe in the intrinsic value of gold and silver. Inflation and political uncertainties have undermined their confidence in paper currencies. To countless investors and speculators, as well as the man in the street, gold and silver still have the attributes of enduring worth.

Prices of gold and silver advanced substantially, if irregularly, during the years after 1971. Previous restrictions on private ownership of gold were lifted by most governments, trading in gold futures was instituted, and trading in silver futures (which had been restored in the sixties) became extremely active. In a single year more silver was traded on two U.S. exchanges than had been mined throughout the world since production began thousands of years ago.

By 1978 the stage was set for the drama of the following two years. That year's average price for gold on the London market was $193 an ounce, about five-and-a-half times the official price under the Bretton Woods agreement prior to 1971. The 1978 average price of silver in New York was $5·40 an ounce — a little more than four times the monetary value that had prevailed in the United States until 1967.

Large though these increases appeared, they were dwarfed by the incredible climb that followed. Chart 8 traces the price movements of gold and silver, month by month, during 1979 and 1980. These figures are the monthly averages, which peaked in January 1980 at $675 an ounce for gold (19 times the earlier IMF official price of $35) and $38·26 an ounce for silver (almost 30 times the U.S. coinage parity of $1·29).

What caused this startling rise? Various factors have been cited. Inflation was rampant throughout the principal industrialized nations, in most cases at double-digit rates. Interest rates were soaring. Currency exchange rates were fluctuating wildly, following the renewed increase in oil prices. The international situation had deteriorated in consequence of the holding of U.S. diplomats and military officers as hostages in Iran. When U.S.S.R. troops entered Afghanistan in late 1979, fears arose of a Soviet drive into other Middle Eastern countries that might precipitate a new World War.

These developments motivated many apprehensive investors to buy precious metals as an alternative to retaining bank accounts

111

CHART 8. GOLD AND SILVER PRICES YEARLY AVERAGES 1978-85

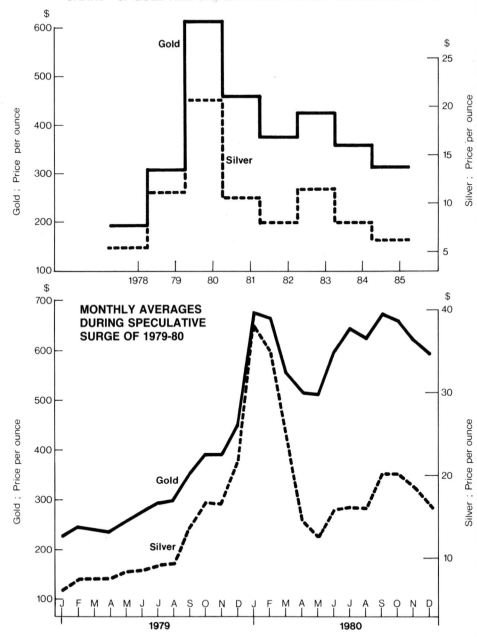

denominated in paper currencies. Traditionally, one would have expected gold to appreciate at least as sharply as silver — since a given weight of gold, readily stored or transported, would be worth many times the same weight of silver.

Instead, as the Chart shows, the price of silver far outperformed the price of gold. In the peak month of January 1980, the silver price was seven times the 1978 average, while gold had increased by three-and-a-half times. The answer to this seeming discrepancy appeared to lie in attempted market manipulation — an effort to corner the silver market.

Most of the gold and silver produced since mining of these metals began is still in existence — as bullion, coins, jewellery, or decorative objects, including gold and silverware. Estimates of these stocks place the global amounts at perhaps three billion ounces of gold and 25 billion ounces of silver. The proportion in bullion and coin form is far greater in gold than in silver. Given the prices of the two metals, it is clear that the resources required for an attempt to corner the market would be smaller for silver than for gold.

The existence of futures markets appears to facilitate such an attempt — since purchases there can be made on margins, the buyer puts up only a fraction of the full cash value of a transaction. Moreover, if the price can be kept on a rising course, the enhanced value of the first purchases can assist in the financing of further purchases.

At any rate, the press published frequent reports in the course of 1979 attributing the rise in silver prices to purchases by the Hunt brothers of Texas, wealthy oil heirs, supported by Arab and Brazilian capitalists. Whether the group acted within the framework of commodity exchange regulations is a question that government authorities have been investigating. Regardless of this issue, clearly the Hunt interests were heavily involved in purchasing silver on margin.

The rising prices had a significant impact on both demand and supply of silver. Supply increased rapidly as holders of coins and silver-containing objects were tempted to sell by the high prices. These legitimate sellers were augmented by a wave of silver thefts.

Stolen family heirlooms were promptly melted down into crude ingots, which were then offered to buyers for secondary refineries. The available capacity for recycling silver was swamped. To capitalize on high prices, sellers hedged by selling forward on the futures exchanges for delivery at a time when they would have refined silver available.

At the same time that this extraordinary increase in supply developed, industrial demand rapidly diminished. As their own sales of finished products declined, manufacturers of silver products bought less metal and cut their in-process inventories to the bone. Particularly pronounced was the collapse of sales of sterling silverware since the price of a single table setting had been pushed far above what a dozen table settings would have cost a few years earlier.

In these circumstances, with more and more silver being offered and other buyers dropping out, the Hunt group found itself unable to support the price at the January peak. As the price of silver began to edge downward, the Hunts were called on to post additional margins. In mid-March it became known that they were unable to meet all their obligations with ready cash. Part of their holdings had to be liquidated, accelerating the price decline. Indeed, a major brokerage firm acting for them was alleged to have been facing the prospect of insolvency.

However, a crisis was averted. Urgent negotiations subsequently evolved an arrangement with banking interests under which Hunt assets, other than silver, were pledged as security for the silver-incurred debts. The remaining Hunt silver holdings were segregated for eventual liquidation (they were actually sold in 1985) and the Hunts agreed to refrain from further activity in silver.

The substantial, but comparatively more modest, rise in gold prices was not accompanied by comparable melodrama. *The widespread theory that gold and silver prices follow parallel trends is not supported by the facts.* True, the broad movements of rise and fall tend to coincide but the extent of the swings in gold may differ greatly from the swings in silver. Thus, after the reverses that occurred in March 1980, gold prices recovered strongly during the third quarter while silver's rebound was comparatively mild.

Many have long believed that a mystic ratio exists between the prices of the two metals. The Romans at one time set the price ratio between silver and gold at 25 : 1; earlier the Kings of Babylon decreed the relationship should be 10 : 1; William Jennings Bryan ran for the Presidency of the United States on a platform that advocated 16 : 1. In the great depression of the thirties the actual ratio was as high as 80 : 1 and in the late sixties it narrowed to less than 20 : 1.

These changes suggest that, in fact, there is no fixed relationship between the prices of the two metals. Instead, the market has set the price ratio at any given time on the basis of a complex of political and economic factors which are themselves highly variable.

The events of 1979-80 strongly intimate that access to margin trading on futures markets was a major factor in the much steeper price rise of silver than of gold. Without the ability to pyramid a long position as the price of silver rose on the commodity exchanges, the effort to corner the silver market would have been far more difficult — if not impossible.

This is not to suggest that wild fluctuations in commodity prices only occur on futures exchanges. Some minerals not traded on the exchanges have had a history of erratic price behaviour — tungsten and cadmium are two examples. Once Amax lost its dominant position in molybdenum, the price of that commodity also became extremely volatile. The change in aluminium's price patterns is not solely the consequence of the inception of futures trading — the entry of many new producers into the market, particularly producers from the developing world, would in any case have had a major impact on aluminium's market trends.

There are those who believe the market should make all economic decisions, that it should be free from regulation or intervention either by private or public sectors and that fluctuating quotations are a small price to pay for liberty in trade. Others, however, see extreme volatility as imposing severe burdens on society — on consumers, producers, and governments. They seek stability in prices as a key to orderly economic progress.

CHAPTER SIX

The Quest for Price Stability

Why Seek to Stabilize Mineral Prices?
Wildly fluctuating mineral prices inhibit orderly economic progress.
The difficulties they have caused for specific mineral industries are
readily documented. Even a relatively short-lived but violent
upheaval, such as the one that occurred in the silver market in
1979-80, has lasting consequences.

During that brief speculative surge, silver miners enjoyed windfall
profits of unprecedented magnitude. But this short period of high
prices cost them the loss of four-fifths of one significant market —
sterling silverware — and serious impairment of demand from other
consuming industries.

Prior to the drama of 1979-80, the manufacture of sterling
silverware had been a constant, dependable, and sizeable outlet for
refined silver. By long tradition, affluent young couples in developed
market-economy countries could expect to receive sterling silverware
as wedding gifts from loving relatives and friends. The size of this
market is indicated by consumption in the United States alone of 17·9
million ounces of silver for sterlingware in 1978, the year before the
events described in the preceding chapter.

The high prices of 1979-80 dealt the sterling silverware industry a
near-mortal blow. Sky-rocketing silver quotations pushed the cost of
silverware beyond the reach of all but the very wealthiest families; it
caused a prolonged rash of silverware burglaries, impelling a drastic
rise in theft insurance premiums, and induced many householders to
store their silverware in bank vaults rather than keep the utensils at
home for daily use.

Newly-weds lost interest in owning sterling silverware. When asked their gift preferences, they specified other luxury items. Even when sterling silverware prices were subsequently reduced as the cost of refined silver fell, buying interest was not rekindled. In 1984, with silver prices down to one-fifth of their 1980 highs, consumption of silver for sterlingware in the United States was only 3·6 million ounces — barely 20% of the 1978 level of consumption.

Manufacturers of sterling silverware and retail merchants had suffered grievous inventory losses in 1979-80 when prices spurted upward and then collapsed. Rather than risk a repetition of that debacle, they have since preferred to concentrate promotion and marketing efforts on substitutes such as stainless steel cutlery.

Meanwhile, high prices had encouraged other silver consuming industries to find substitute materials — and many had achieved a measure of success, although in no other case was the reduction in demand as pronounced as in sterling silver.

The short-lived speculative binge caused grave discomfort to the government of at least one silver-producing nation. In the early seventies the Peruvian Government had pre-empted marketing of all mineral exports — including silver. The government marketing corporation, Minpeco, decided in mid-1979 to embark on a programme of forward silver sales on COMEX, when the price reached $10 an ounce. The price looked high to the organization's managers. That it would quadruple within six months was something they, like most market observers, simply did not anticipate.

As prices advanced, margin calls were issued on forward sales already made. Minpeco continued to sell current production and in addition to make still more forward sales. By late 1979 much of Peru's cash reserve was tied up in margin deposits. As prices continued to advance, a sudden reversal in policy was decided on. The officials decided they had best cover their outstanding contracts — which in effect meant buying back what had been earlier sold at lower prices. The losses involved were in the tens of millions of dollars. Allegations of impropriety were made against Minpeco's management, although the more probable cause of the losses was inexperience in dealing with the market and the unprecedented price rise.

A few years prior to silver's dizzy climb, a similar rise had taken place in the price of another mineral — cobalt. A far smaller and more concentrated industry than silver, cobalt is used primarily in high technology applications. The major source of cobalt supplies has long been central Africa. Over 50% of global output originates in Zaire, formerly the Belgian Congo.

When a group of insurgents invaded the copper-cobalt mining district of Shaba Province, Zaire, in 1977, panic ensued because of grave uncertainties over the continuity of cobalt supply (the effect on copper was relatively minor, as only 6% to 7% of world supply originates in Zaire). The cobalt price soared in a few days from a previous level of $6 a pound to more than $40 a pound in merchant markets — while the so-called official price rose to $25 a pound, with quantities at that price tightly rationed among the established customers.

In fact, the hostile occupation of the mining areas was relatively brief, order was restored, and normal production resumed within a few months. Prices eventually receded to levels in line with trends in competing commodities.

Nevertheless, the invasion and the sharp price rise caused users to ponder their long-term cobalt requirements. Recognizing that they were heavily dependent for cobalt on a developing country with grave political problems, consumers redoubled their efforts to find new sources or to develop substitutes. Production outside Zaire increased and markets shrank. Consumption in the market-economy countries now averages about 30% below its pre-crisis level.

These developments in both the silver and cobalt markets represent reaction to a single episode of brief yet sharp price advance. Other minerals have experienced repeated periods of wildly fluctuating quotations. Their price charts show cycles of sharp peaks and deep valleys, approximately paralleling swings in the broad business cycle.

Sustained volatility exacerbates the normal problems of producing and consuming industries. It has a devastating impact on the economies of nations heavily dependent on export revenues arising from a single price-volatile commodity. The recent history of the copper industry provides a representative illustration of these problems.

The Copper Experience

Copper, the oldest industrial material known to man, can be considered the archetype of volatile mineral industries. Among metals, copper ranks third in volume of world production after steel and aluminium. Since copper ores are much lower grade than either steel or aluminium, the key to success in copper is the ability to find and equip viable deposits. After discovery, managements are faced with enormous capital requirements and extended periods of time to develop mines and build processing facilities. Often, as has already been commented, extensive infrastructure must be provided for power, transport, and staff housing.

In making a decision to proceed, managements must predict the unpredictable — the future price of copper in relation to estimated production costs, including a return on invested capital.

Despite these uncertainties, despite fluctuating prices, the world copper industry almost tripled in size during the post-War period 1950-73. The average 4% annual rate of growth in global copper consumption was, of course, the spur to this expansion. Prices, reflecting economic growth, rose strongly in the mid-fifties and again in the mid-sixties. Occasional evidence of spot shortages caused some to believe that as known copper reserves were depleted a protracted squeeze might develop.

However, in reality more ore was being found than was being mined. Numerous new deposits became available for exploitation by those willing to risk the uncertainties surrounding the industry. In the late sixties and early seventies, encouraged by rising prices, a plethora of projects came to the fore, many of them involving investments of hundreds of millions of dollars and taking from three to six years to bring to fruition. The decisions to proceed were made on the assumption that the 4% growth in consumption would continue and that copper prices would roughly keep pace with inflation in the principal developed market-economy countries.

119

These expectations did not materialize. The energy crisis of 1974 and the recession that followed caused a slow-down in industrial growth. Technological changes reduced the intensity of use of most minerals, copper included, in relation to gross national product. Inflation rates soared because of rising energy costs, deficit financing by most nations, mounting interest rates, and general currency instability.

Yet prices of copper and many other commodities lagged far behind the rate of inflation. The discrepancy was due to excess capacity and unwieldy inventories on the commodity exchanges and in producers' hands, as has already been described.

The onset of a second severe recession in 1981 sounded the death knell for many copper enterprises. Some of these were old, long-established producers that had earned substantial profits in the past. Others were newly-launched projects, investments which had to be written off in whole or in part. The Twin Buttes, Lake Shore, Carr Fork and Copper Flat projects in the United States and the Granduc mine in Canada, all started in the sixties and seventies, are examples of what might be called industrial infant mortality. Their unfortunate owners had received little or no return on their large investments. The mines have been closed — if at some future date market conditions improve so that re-opening appears feasible, substantial new investments will be necessary.

In the public sector area, the Peruvian Government launched two projects that have been financial disasters — the Cerro Verde mine and the expansion of the Cobriza mine. Production has been continued at both but it involves substantial losses. In Mexico, the Caridad project, in which the government holds a large stake, has struggled to meet interest payments on its huge debt. In Iran, the level of production and the financial status of the Sar Cheshmeh project are shrouded in secrecy under the Khomeini Government, but it is very unlikely that the investment cost of $1,400 million poured into the undertaking under the previous Government of the Shah can be recovered.

Many surviving copper mines have resorted to such expedients as mining ore of better than average grade or postponing needed mine preparation or equipment maintenance — thus deferring expenses that will eventually have to be incurred.

Both the shut-down of mines with remaining unmined resources and the high-grading of mines still operating are undesirable from the viewpoint of the strict conservationist. These measures mitigate against the fullest eventual recovery of the world's finite copper resources for the use of future generations.

In the face of unstable prices, consuming industries have difficulties in planning materials selection. For a given application copper may be the most efficient material at a given price. When copper prices rise, a substitute material may seem preferable. If the manufacturer substitutes another material and copper prices subsequently decline, should he revert to copper? Changes in material selection are costly to implement — they involve alterations in design, in production equipment, and in the application of labour skills.

If a manufacturer decides that superior performance dictates that he remain wedded to copper as a raw material regardless of cost, wildly fluctuating prices are disturbing. They create the possibility of inventory write-downs in periods of receding prices or of increased cash tie-up when prices rise. Moreover, the consuming industry is faced with frequent adjustments to sales prices and grave difficulty in maintaining profit margins.

Unstable copper prices create major problems for governments of countries which depend on copper exports for a major share of their foreign exchange earnings and tax revenues. These include Chile, Zambia, Zaire, Peru, and the Philippines. When copper prices were strong in 1973 and early 1974, they enjoyed improving trade balances. Government budgets were increased as tax collections rose. Payment of interest on foreign debt was facilitated.

The subsequent collapse of copper prices cut sharply into both foreign exchange earnings and tax revenues. The foreign debt interest and amortization payments became an onerous problem. All five countries had to borrow through the Compensatory Financing Facility of the International Monetary Fund. This facility represents bridging loans made by the IMF in Special Drawing Rights (SDR) to assist governments that have experienced balance of payment problems as a consequence of low prices for their principal commodity exports. As of April 30, 1986, six countries had CFF loans outstanding to the IMF totalling SDR1,155 million, equivalent to $U.S.1,364 million. These were tied into problems arising from loss of copper export earnings.

Except for the Philippines, these countries had joined in 1967 in the formation of CIPEC, an organization that has repeatedly expressed an interest in finding a formula to stabilize copper prices. However, with the exception of a brief unsuccessful effort in 1975, no concerted steps to evolve a programme have been taken by the CIPEC members. In the absence of such a programme, these governments and their public sector companies have followed a policy of maintaining copper production at effective capacity in an effort to maximize export earnings. As previously indicated, this policy has helped to create unwieldy inventory surpluses at times of reduced demand and has been a major factor in the depressed copper prices that have prevailed for much of the period since the onset of the energy crisis.

Thus, producers, consumers, and governments involved with minerals all have reasons for desiring price stability but they are faced with the reality that prices for most minerals tend to be unstable — in some cases extremely unstable. What can be done to reduce price fluctuations?

Pharaoh's Dream
The Bible records in some detail an early attempt to achieve economic stability. The reigning Pharaoh of Egypt had a disturbing dream in which seven lean cattle ate seven fat cattle. Startled by its vivid pictures, he asked his Hebrew servant, Joseph, for an interpretation. Joseph stated that the dream predicted seven years of good crops and economic prosperity to be followed (and, in fact, swallowed up) by seven years of poor crops and economic difficulties.

Joseph suggested that Pharaoh stockpile a share of the crops of the good years as protection against the poor years to come. The argument was persuasive. Pharaoh decreed that one-fifth of the crops in the good years be set aside and held for the poor years to come — in effect a buffer stock. According to the Bible, this not only tided Egypt over the years of meagre harvests, it also enabled that country to export some of its buffer stocks to assist neighbouring countries.

The Bible is silent on the question of prices for the crops stored and subsequently sold. As an absolute autocrat, Pharaoh presumably could fix prices paid for the buffer stocks, could levy taxes to finance the project, and could decide when and at what prices to sell.

In the modern world only the governments of the centrally-planned countries under Communist rule possess similar powers. A subsequent chapter deals with the mineral industries of this group of countries. The market-economy countries have fewer options in trying to cope with price instability.

The Diamond Approach
Perhaps the closest approach to Pharaoh's plan has been the remarkable marketing system developed in the diamond industry. This industry is dominated by a group called the Central Selling Organization, controlled by De Beers, a prominent South African diamond mining firm. De Beers and its affiliates account for perhaps half of the world's production of gem and industrial diamonds. Much of the balance is bought by the Central Selling Organization from other producers for subsequent re-sale.

A development in Australia is an illustration of the CSO's powers of persuasion. In the early eighties major diamond deposits were discovered in Western Australia by mining firms not affiliated with De Beers. The original marketing plans evolved by the finders, in association with the Government of Australia, were to sell independently of CSO. However, as work proceeded in preparation for production, a change of heart took place. By the time production began, agreement was reached that all gem stones and 75% of industrials from Western Australia would be marketed by CSO.

De Beers has maintained its hold on the diamond market over many years thanks to marketing skills and a willingness to hold inventories and to adjust its own production at times when demand either for gems or industrial diamonds diminished. The value of diamonds could readily be undercut by competitive selling during slack times. De Beers has been able to persuade competitive producers that prolonged weakness in diamond prices would destroy the gems' attraction as long-term investments.

This approach has worked well for De Beers and the diamond producers. It has maintained public confidence in diamonds as investments and it has stabilized revenues from diamond exports of several developing countries. It has not, however, commended itself to the anti-trust division of the U.S. Department of Justice, which considers the CSO to be a cartel inconsistent with the existing anti-monopoly laws of the United States. Efforts to institute legal proceedings have thus far been unsuccessful, since neither De Beers nor the CSO maintains offices within the United States.

Efforts to control other mineral markets through monopolies or cartel-like producer organizations have been tried on numerous occasions but none has been able to duplicate the De Beers record of successful longevity. In some cases failure has been the consequence of economic forces; in others, legal action has actually disbanded the so-called trusts. Thus, in the United States, Standard Oil was broken up into several component units, each of which has been successful on its own and competes vigorously with other Standard-bred concerns. They survive today under the names of Exxon, Chevron, Sohio, Amoco, and Mobil — all mammoth petroleum enterprises. Aluminum Company of America was forced to spin off its Canadian properties as Alcan. Although both continue as leaders in the world aluminium industry, they compete with each other and with a dozen other major aluminium producers.

Producer Associations
World-wide producer associations represent a somewhat different approach to the effort to control markets. In these organizations competitors band together in an effort to stabilize market conditions by acting in concert on production and price policies. In some cases the associations represent individual enterprises but in recent years it

has been more common for them to represent the governments of the countries that are the chief producers and/or exporters of the commodity in question.

OPEC, the oil exporters' association, is the prototype of such organizations. Although this book deals primarily with non-fuel minerals, a brief recital of OPEC's recent history illustrates the inherent problems that develop when an effort is made to control market forces through a world-wide producer association. Moreover, the experience with OPEC is fresh in the minds of most people.

When OPEC made its dramatic move to triple prices of crude oil overnight in 1974, oil-consuming countries appeared powerless to cope with the OPEC decision. The organization represented 11 of the chief oil-exporting nations; oil was essential to meet the energy, transportation and heating needs of all countries; and while there were other important producers who did not belong to the group, they could meet only a fraction of global needs.

For the seven years 1974-80 OPEC's price decisions set the market. But as prices rose, oil demand began first to level off and then to decrease. High prices stimulated more efficient use of oil and encouraged substitution of other energy sources. High prices also encouraged a sizeable increase in non-OPEC oil production.

Gradually it became clear that a significant oil surplus was developing. OPEC tried to deal with the situation by establishing production quotas for its members to restrict supplies. In time, some member countries, anxious to maximize revenues, failed to observe their individual production limits. Others, not wishing to accumulate unsold stocks, began making special price concessions to lure buyers. By 1982 weakness in the price structure had become widespread. OPEC readjusted its prices downward that year for the first time since 1974.

Market weakness has persisted. Only the willingness of Saudi Arabia to yield market share for a time by limiting its output prevented an outright collapse of the OPEC organization. Each time the members convene for their semi-annual conferences speculation arises whether the organization will survive. Two members — Iraq and Iran — have been engaged in active military hostilities for several

125

years. Each is endeavouring to damage the other's oil facilities and thus undermine their opponent's economy.

The OPEC experience reveals that in times of adversity producer associations have difficulty in maintaining discipline. Members have economic incentives to ignore limitations on volume and to shade prices. Moreover, since such organizations rarely encompass all producers of the given commodity, non-members are free to produce as much as they choose and to sell at whatever price they deem expedient. Buyers of the commodity seek to substitute other materials or to economize on its use to lessen their vulnerability to an association's unilateral price decisions.

Inter-Governmental Producer/Consumer Associations

Some countries believe commodity agreements are more effective if consumers as well as producers participate. Indeed, during the post-War era, the United Nations has repeatedly discussed the desirability of such producer/consumer associations.

In the spring of 1974 a special session of the United Nations discussed commodity problems in the light of developing concerns about oil prices. Many believed that arrangements similar to OPEC would be tried by producers of other commodities. Articles in the business press, predicting success in establishing cartels for such minerals as bauxite, copper, manganese, mercury and many others, have already been cited.

The industrialized countries urged that any commodity arrangements should include governments of consuming as well as producing nations. The developing nations seized on this idea as an opportunity to persuade the industrialized countries to provide funding for commodity buffer stocks — the method used by Pharaoh.

They proposed establishing an international Common Fund to finance buffer stocks of many commodities and to be administered through the United Nations Conference on Trade and Development (UNCTAD).

A list of 18 commodities was proposed to be covered by the Common Fund. Thirteen were agricultural items and five were minerals (bauxite, copper, iron ore, manganese and tin). Each commodity was to be the subject of a separate formal commodity agreement, involving the principal consuming and producing nations of that commodity.

The initial proposal was to raise $6,000 million for the Common Fund from U.N. member nations. This figure was substantially scaled down at the subsequent conferences called to review the plan. Financial stringencies affecting the principal countries involved have proved an insurmountable obstacle. Despite prolonged debate, the plan is not yet in effect as it has not been ratified by the required number of governments. As of this writing, neither the Soviet Union nor the United States has ratified.

Nevertheless, finding a way to reduce volatility of commodity prices continues to be a goal that fascinates and preoccupies governments and industrialists. In certain quarters — anti-trust lawyers, some economists, most traders and speculators — interference with the free determination of commodity prices by the ebb and flow of market forces is anathema. But producers, consumers and government officials — faced with the often cruel consequences of extreme price movements — remain interested in finding a way to ameliorate problems caused by extreme price fluctuations.

Meanwhile, even if the UNCTAD Common Fund is not available, several international commodity agreements have been negotiated. Only one of these — the International Tin Agreement — has involved a mineral.

The Effort to Stabilize Tin Prices

In October 1985, the International Tin Council announced suspension of its buffer stock operation in tin metal. This effectively ended a 29-year effort to stabilize tin prices by an organization encompassing both the chief tin producing countries (principally developing nations) and the chief tin consuming countries (all industrialized nations).

Although the Council membership consisted of sovereign governments, the organization suspended operations because it could not meet its financial obligations. As a consequence, lending institutions and metal dealing firms that had dealt with the Council's buffer stock sustained enormous losses. The London Metal Exchange ceased trading in tin, the price plunged precipitously, mines were closed with massive unemployment ensuing, and the large stocks of tin overhanging the market threatened a sustained period of depressed quotations.

Much can be learned from a study of this international effort to control the price of a commodity through inter-governmental agreements. It was the first such attempt in the mineral kingdom. The motives that led to the formation of the first International Tin Agreement in 1956 were certainly well intentioned. The tin producers, a group of developing nations with severe economic problems, wanted stable tin prices so that their mining industries could provide secure employment and a steady flow of export revenues. The tin consumers, as industrial nations importing their tin supplies, sought assured access to adequate supplies at reasonable and predictable prices.

Why not sit down and work out a scheme to put a floor under prices of tin that would ensure the viability of the mines and a ceiling over prices of tin that would permit consumers to maximize markets for products containing the metal?

Prior to World War II a tin price stabilization scheme had been tried by leading tin producing countries. Established in 1931 as the International Tin Committee, it involved control of supplies through a system of export quotas, plus market support through a buffer stock operation. During the years of the great depression this arrangement succeeded in keeping tin prices within a fairly moderate range, as contrasted with sharper fluctuations in prices of other base metals.

The arrangements lapsed during World War II, when three of the principal tin producing countries were occupied by Japanese military forces. Following the end of the war, there were discussions about reviving the Committee. However, the principal consuming countries suggested that in its place arrangements should be worked out that would include them as members. An International Study Group, including both consumers and producers, first met in 1947. For a time, the Korean War and massive tin buying for the United States' strategic stockpile combined to create a strong tin market. When these influences abated in the mid-fifties concern over future tin price trends surfaced once again. Finally, proposals for an international agreement took concrete form in 1956.

The new organization, known as the International Tin Council, included both tin producing and tin consuming countries. The first agreement covered a period of five years. Subsequent agreements were also for five-year periods, each agreement being subject to ratification by the member nations.

The agreements had the stated objective of avoiding persistent dis-equilibrium between production and consumption of tin and the accumulation of burdensome stocks. They were intended to stabilize employment in the tin producing and consuming countries, maintain steady export revenues for the governments of producing countries, and minimize price fluctuations.

Under the Council rules, producing and consuming members shared equally in decisions. A total of 2,000 votes was divided — 1,000 votes for producers and 1,000 votes for consumers. Within each division, votes were distributed among members in proportion to their tonnages of production or consumption. The number of members has varied considerably. Originally there were six producer and ten consumer members. At the time of the Fifth Agreement (1976-81) this had grown to seven producer and 22 consumer members. Under the Sixth Agreement, effective in 1982, fewer nations participated. On major issues, a two-thirds majority was required from both producers and consumers voting independently — thus ensuring that approved measures were acceptable to both producers and consumers.

Meetings of the Council were held at frequent intervals. A prime order of business normally was a review of the statistical position of tin, followed by decisions as to the price range within which the Council would endeavour to control the market.

The Council set both floor and ceiling prices for tin. Within this broad range there was a middle zone — intended to represent a 'normal' price for the metal. The weapons used by the Council to maintain price equilibrium were export controls and buffer stocks. Export controls were invoked after minimum stocks had been acquired by the buffer stock and when statistical projections suggested that production would exceed consumption by a sufficient margin to result in burdensome stock build-ups. Each producing country was assigned a standard quota representing its export potential when producing at effective capacity. If export limitations were decided on, the Council established a percentage to be applied to the standard quota. Producer members were expected to hold exports at or below that percentage.

Originally the buffer stock was financed entirely by the producer members. At the inception of each five-year agreement, producer members contributed in proportion to their share of the aggregate assigned quotas. Under the first agreement, £16,900,000 in total funds (or tin metal equivalent) was called for. A producing country whose quota was 10% of the aggregate therefore was expected to contribute £1,690,000. At the termination of each agreement, the manager of the buffer stock calculated the aggregate value of the stock still held plus his cash, if any. Appropriate credits were issued which members could apply to meet obligations under the succeeding agreement.

Consumer members originally made no contribution to the buffer stock. Later some consumer countries made voluntary contributions, thus increasing funds available for the buffer stock. Under the Sixth Agreement the consumer members were obliged to contribute to the buffer stock. The initial levy under the first agreement had been equal to about 25,000 tons of tin, about one-sixth of world production, then about 150,000 tons annually.

Operation of Price Trigger Points Under Tin Agreements
Under the agreements, to the extent that funds were available, the buffer stock had to buy when the market price was equal to or below the agreement floor price. Similarly, if the price was equal to or above the agreement ceiling price, the buffer had to sell and continue to do so until either the price fell or the buffer stock had been exhausted.

When the price was between the floor and ceiling prices, the buffer stock manager could buy or sell — provided that he was a net seller in the upper range (i.e. between the middle zone and the ceiling price) and he was a net buyer in the lower range (i.e. between the floor price and the middle zone).

Under the first five agreements, the buffer stock had earned trading profits, as purchases were made when prices were at the low end of the trading range and sales were made at the high end of the range. The buffer stock also earned interest whenever it had a cash balance in reserve. Despite these gains, as tin prices rose over the years, progressively larger levies were needed to finance buffer stock operations under each successive agreement. This became a serious burden for heavily indebted producer governments.

The largest of the tin consuming nations, the United States, had a markedly ambivalent attitude toward the Council. It declined to join the first four agreements, although its observers were present at the meetings at which the agreements were negotiated. Two motives accounted for the U.S. abstention. One was the objection of U.S. anti-trust officials to the export quota arrangements, which were viewed as inconsistent with U.S. legislation that makes agreements to restrict supplies illegal.

The second was the attitude of large U.S. tin consuming industries. They felt the agreements tended to favour producers and would lead to unjustifiably high prices. A further factor was the fear that membership would open the door for efforts by the Council to intervene in matters relating to the large U.S. strategic stockpile holdings of tin.

Despite these reservations, the United States joined the Fifth Agreement in 1976. The State Department persuaded the U.S. Senate to ratify membership on the grounds that it would promote improved dialogue with the Third World tin producing nations.

However, once a member, the United States found that its policies on tin matters were viewed with suspicion — particularly by the Bolivian delegation. The Bolivians objected to the large bloc of consumer votes assigned to the United States and to the U.S. attitude on discussions of changes in floor and ceiling prices.

**TABLE 7: TIN FLOOR AND CEILING PRICES ESTABLISHED BY
THE INTERNATIONAL TIN COUNCIL**

Date	Floor Price £ per ton	U.S. Dollar Equivalent $ per lb	Ceiling Price £ per ton	U.S. Dollar Equivalent $ per lb
Original (1956)	640	0·80	880	1·10
March, 1957	730	0·9125	880	1·10
January, 1962	790	0·9875	965	1·20625
December, 1963	850	1·0625	1,000	1·25
November, 1964	1,000	1·25	1,200	1·50
July, 1966	1,100	1·375	1,400	1·75
November, 1967	1,283*	1·375	1,633	1·75
January, 1968	1,280	1·375	1,630	1·75
October, 1970	1,350	1·45	1,650	1·77

In 1972, because of weakness in the pound sterling, the International Tin Council decided to establish floor and ceiling prices based on the Malaysian dollar (the ringgit), since this was felt to be representative of conditions affecting tin production in southeast Asia, the principal producing area. The new quotations were in Malaysian dollars per picul—a Malaysian unit of weight equivalent to 133·3 lb of tin.

	M$	$	M$	$
July, 1972	583	1·90	718	2·34
September, 1973	635	2·07	760	2·47
May, 1974	850	2·69	1,050	3·32
January, 1975	900	2·94	1,100	3·59
March, 1976	950	2·78	1,100	3·22
May, 1976	1,000	2·94	1,200	3·53
December, 1976	1,075	3·19	1,325	3·94
July, 1977	1,200	3·64	1,500	4·55
July, 1978	1,350	4·40	1,700	5·54
July, 1979	1,500	5·25	1,950	6·82
March, 1980	1,650	5·78	2,145	7·51
October, 1981	1,765	5·60	2,290	7·25

In converting the floor and ceiling prices into U.S. dollars from either pounds sterling or Malaysian dollars, the conversion has been at the rate of exchange prevailing at the time the new support levels were announced. Thus, on occasion the higher floor and ceiling prices stated in pounds or Malaysian dollars has meant little or no change in these prices in dollar terms.

With regard to the three intermediate ranges — i.e., buying, neutral or selling zones — in general these have been established by dividing the spread between floor and ceiling prices equally. Thus, initially the buying zone was between £640 and £720; and the selling zone was between £800 and £880.

* In November, 1967, the floor and ceiling prices represented an interim decision pending clarification of the new conversion rate between pounds sterling and dollars.

When negotiations on a Sixth Agreement began, the United States suggested that provisions for export quota limitations be deleted and replaced by a greatly increased buffer stock. These changes were not acceptable to the majority. The long debate delayed endorsement of a Sixth Agreement, the Fifth Agreement had to be extended for a year, and the Sixth Agreement only became effective June 30, 1982, on a provisional basis due to delays in ratification by some of the members.

Neither the United States nor Bolivia became members of the Sixth Agreement. Indeed, for a time, the heated discussions and the difficult market situation in early 1982 made it appear possible that there would be no agreement.

From its inception, the Council had recognized that changing circumstances might require occasional adjustment of the ranges within which it would endeavour to contain tin prices. A single fixed price was never contemplated. Rather, members agreed that the market should be allowed to reflect the ebb and flow of supply and demand but that it would be desirable to put a floor under and a ceiling over the market price.

Table 7 records the dates at which the Council first established and subsequently altered the floor and ceiling prices. As shown, the standards were originally expressed in pounds sterling, to mirror tin quotations on the London Metal Exchange. In 1972 weakness in sterling caused the Council to switch to the Malaysian currency as the yardstick for measuring price. Even though the Malaysian dollar is hardly a widely accepted world currency unit, it seemed an appropriate choice because the bulk of global tin supply is mined in south-east Asia. Penang (Malaysia) is where a substantial share of that supply is marketed.

The floor and ceiling prices, whether in pounds or Malaysian dollars, have been translated into U.S. dollars to make comparisons clearer. In the era of floating exchange rates since 1971 the dollar has also been subject to fluctuation in value in relation to other currencies. However, since the United States is the largest consumer of tin, prices in U.S. currency have had considerable relevance for the tin industry.

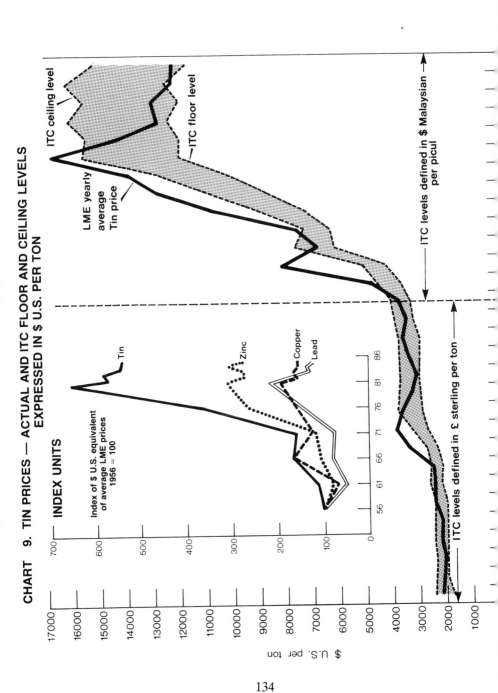

CHART 9. TIN PRICES — ACTUAL AND ITC FLOOR AND CEILING LEVELS
EXPRESSED IN $ U.S. PER TON

ITC ceiling level

ITC floor level

LME yearly average Tin price

ITC levels defined in $ Malaysian per picul

ITC levels defined in £ sterling per ton

INDEX UNITS

Index of $ U.S. equivalent of average LME prices 1956 = 100

Tin

Zinc

Copper

Lead

56 61 66 71 76 81 86

$ U.S. per ton

Effectiveness of Tin Price Floors and Ceilings

On one occasion the price of tin fell below the agreed floor price for an extended period. This occurred in 1958, when the Soviet Union shipped large amounts of tin into Western Europe, primarily of metal it had received from the People's Republic of China, presumably in payment for military supplies furnished by the Soviets during the Chinese Revolution. Neither the U.S.S.R. nor China were members of the Council at the time. Strong protests by the Council persuaded the Soviet Union to modify its export programme. The price of tin rose above the ITC floor within a few months and consistently remained above the floor until buffer stock operations ceased.

The record in defending the tin agreement ceiling prices is strikingly different. The market price exceeded the ceilings for protracted periods in 1963-65, in 1973-74, and in 1976-80. As provided by the agreement rules, on each occasion sales were made by the buffer stock manager as the price approached the agreed ceiling levels. In each of the three instances selling continued until all buffer stocks had been liquidated. Once stocks were exhausted, the ITC lacked means to prevent further sharp advances — even though there had also been substantial sales from the U.S. tin stockpile.

One suggestion is that consuming countries should impose import limitations to defend the price ceilings, just as export limitations are used by producers to defend the price floors. Yet import limitations could be counter-productive to the long-run interests of producers. They might hasten substitution of other materials in place of tin.

After each experience with prices above ceilings, the Council in due course adopted higher floor and ceiling prices in its endeavour to keep its ranges in line with the actual market. However, in subsequent downturns in the business cycle, the new higher floor price remained in effect supported by the use of buffer stock purchases and export limitations. Other metals had no comparable support mechanisms to prevent prices from receding to previous low levels. Thus, for metals such as copper, lead and zinc in periods of economic decline prices fell rapidly.

Chart 9 illustrates the record of tin prices since 1956 as compared with the prices of copper, lead and zinc. The divergence is striking. In

1956 the price of tin was 2·4 times the price of copper, 6·8 times the price of lead, and more than eight times the price of zinc. In 1985 it averaged 8·7 times the copper price, 31 times the lead price and 15·9 times the zinc price.

If the international agreements while they were in effect did succeed in achieving a high level of prices for tin in relation to prices of other base metals, that success was not achieved without adverse consequences.

High prices stimulated tin production outside the producer country members. Brazil emerged as a significant source after 1970. The United Kingdom as a consumer member was not subject to export limitations and its modest output began rising in the early eighties. Canada, another consumer member, developed a major new deposit that began producing in 1985. Bolivia refused to join the Sixth Agreement and thus was no longer bound by export quotas. Hence, when export limitations were imposed as a consequence of the 1981-82 recession, the remaining producer members were forced to adopt drastic export cutbacks to keep a balanced market.

Even more severe was the effect of price on consumption. Not only did tin consumption fall in the 1981-82 recession, it failed to improve when general economic activity recovered. As previously indicated in the discussion of the Paley Report, tin consumption during the 1950-73 expansionary period had recorded the lowest rate of growth of any major mineral. Between 1973 and 1985 tin consumption in the market-economy countries declined nearly 25%, again much the poorest showing of any major mineral.

Consequently, under the Sixth Agreement, the effort to protect the floor level became increasingly difficult. The Council set export limitations in 1983 at 39·2% below quotas. A substantial level of illegal exports developed, estimated by the Council at 11,400 tons in 1984 (about 8% of the annual market of 160,000 tons). Most of this tonnage was marketed through Singapore, located within easy reach of the three major tin producing countries of Malaysia, Thailand and Indonesia.

The buffer stock manager had to buy heavy offerings of tin in his effort to support the price. As of June 30, 1982, the buffer stock amounted to 49,385 tons — some of which had been financed by borrowing as member contributions had been exhausted. At the end of 1984 the buffer stock had risen to 61,822 tons. Of this, 23,707 tons represented unliquidated balances under the Fifth Agreement and 38,115 tons was related to the Sixth Agreement.

Recourse to Borrowings in Effort to Support Tin Price

Buying continued during 1985. This had to be financed entirely with borrowed money. At floor prices the Sixth Agreement member contributions were only equal to a buffer stock capacity of slightly less than 40,000 tons. Metal in the buffer stock was pledged as collateral against the borrowed funds.

This posed the familiar conundrum. If tin prices could only be maintained through continuing to buy and adding to buffer stocks, which in turn were pledged as collateral for further loans, the buffer stock manager had a tiger by the tail. A cessation of buying would remove the underpinnings from the price. When the price fell, the collateral would be insufficient to cover the loan. In this instance the lenders apparently had felt secure because the borrower was an international organization with more than a score of sovereign nations as members.

However, when the Council suspended its purchases in 1985 because it had run out of funds, Tin Agreement member governments were not prepared to back up the organization's position. They turned down a proposal to contribute additional funds in co-ordination with lending institutions and metal dealing firms to permit an orderly liquidation. Five months of fruitless discussions ensued. In the end, many metal dealers wrote off losses of millions of pounds, the London Metal Exchange imposed a settlement of all outstanding tin contracts at a price of £6,250 a ton (compared with a price of £8,740 a ton prevailing prior to suspension), tin was dropped from the list of metals traded on the LME, and lending institutions took title to the tin they held as collateral.

Since the termination of LME trading tin is being sold directly to consumers by producers and merchants at negotiated prices. Six months after trading was suspended, the prices prevailing in Europe and the United States were less than half the floor price agreed under the Sixth Agreement.

In theory, tin appeared to be the logical mineral with which to try an experiment in international commodity agreements. Roughly 90% of all tin production in the market-economy world crosses an international boundary *en route* to market. This is quite different from most commodities. An international agreement for aluminium or copper, for example, would be made difficult because of the large indigenous production of these metals by some major consuming countries.

Some may argue that the failure of the Tin Agreement arose because of staff shortcomings. It is claimed that the buffer stock management exceeded its authority and so caused the difficulties that ensued. However, mis-management is an ever-present risk inherent in any human endeavour. It could well occur in any arrangement, no matter how tightly drawn.

A more fundamental defect in the Tin Agreement was the attempt to maintain unrealistic price ranges. Prices were periodically revised upward. Not once in its 29-year existence did the Council reduce the floor price. The developing country producers pressed for ever higher prices to meet their urgent needs for foreign currency earnings. The industrialized consuming members failed to resist that pressure — doubtless motivated by a desire to assist the developing countries. The mistake was to overlook the unfortunate consequences of high tin prices in competition with other commodities. The motives of desiring to help poorer countries may have been generous but the consequences of acquiescing to unrealistic price floors has been disastrous.

Even before the suspension of buffer stock purchases in 1985, the problems experienced under the tin arrangements had been noted by producers and consumers of other minerals. Despite frequent conferences since 1973, no consensus has developed for international agreements on bauxite, copper, iron ore or manganese, the other minerals identified as potential participants in the UNCTAD Common Fund. There is a long-standing International Study Group for

Zinc and Lead. It holds periodic meetings to assess the prospects for the two metals but has made no real effort to implement a price-stabilization plan. Sporadic efforts have been made by the principal tungsten producing countries to interest tungsten consumers in a joint effort, but these have not gone beyond the talking stage.

Greater stability of prices remains a hope for metal producers, consumers, and interested governments. They find frequent or violent price fluctuations disruptive. But the key to stability has not yet been found.

CHAPTER SEVEN

Some Exceptional Minerals — The Non-Metallics

A Major Sector of the Mining Industry

The preceding chapters have stressed the cyclical nature of the minerals industries and the unstable pattern of many mineral prices. These generalities do not necessarily apply to all minerals. The precious metals — gold and silver — have at times enjoyed rising prices and good demand when prices of other metals have faltered.

Many of the important non-metallic minerals are also exceptions. Although not immune to the influence of the business cycle, consumption of non-metallics tends to be more stable and prices of non-metallics tend to exhibit less volatility than the consumption and prices of the metallic minerals. Moreover, on a secular basis, several non-metallic minerals are showing sustained market growth.

The public is inclined to think of coal or metals when mining is mentioned. Yet in volume of material mined, the non-metallic industry is actually larger than either the coal industry or the aggregate of the metal mining industries. Employment in and gross sales revenues of non-metallic mining are fully comparable with coal and the metals. Despite low unit value of most bulk non-metallics and the high transport costs involved in moving them to market, international commerce is substantial in many of these commodities.

The number of non-metallic minerals used in the world economy is very large — literally hundreds of distinctive commodities. To attempt to describe each of these industries would be an encyclopaedic task, far beyond the scope of this volume.

At one extreme are some of the bulk materials used in the construction industry. Such products as sand and gravel, crushed stone and cement are produced in virtually every country. They are so readily available at low unit prices that only minor amounts enter into world commerce. The economic and political characteristics that influence their production and consumption differ sharply from those of the internationally traded minerals.

At the other extreme are the gemstones. Statistical information on quantities and values of most gemstones is limited because much production is not reported to governments and prices paid for individual stones vary so widely. Except for diamonds, gemstones are not major factors in the national economies of the producing nations. In the case of diamonds, a large volume of lower quality stones is used for industrial purposes. The aggregate of gem and industrial diamonds plays a significant role in employment and gross production values in such countries as South Africa, Namibia, Zaire, Angola, Botswana, Sierra Leone and, in the past few years, Australia.

Between the two extremes of the bulk building materials and the high value gemstones, however, there is a substantial group of major commodities that share many of the attributes of the metallic minerals. Production of most originates from a few well-defined sources. Consumption is widely distributed around the world. Thus, these minerals are important components of international trade. In several countries they contribute significantly to the gross national product.

The technology involved in mining and processing non-metallic minerals is to a large extent similar to the technology of the metal mining industries. One exception, perhaps, is that solution mining techniques are currently in use for several non-metallic minerals, common salt and potash for instance. The unique Frasch process accounts for a large share of world sulphur production. The process involves pumping hot water through specially drilled wells to melt underground deposits. The molten sulphur is then forced to the surface with compressed air.

However, the great bulk of non-metallic mining activity is carried on by openpit or underground operations using the same types of mining and materials handling equipment as are employed in metal mines. In preparing non-metallic minerals for market, ore-dressing techniques are roughly akin to those involved in the metal mining industries. Because most non-metallic mineral operations start with relatively high content material, ore-dressing is designed primarily to remove minor quantities of impurities — unlike the situation in metal mining which in many instances treats low-grade ores to recover high-grade concentrates. Only in a few instances among non-metallics — asbestos for example — is the feed material to the milling plant low grade, requiring the handling of large tonnages to recover comparatively small amounts of saleable product.

Non-metallic industries do not require the expensive facilities for smelting and refining that account for a large share of the capital and operating costs of the metal producers. Nevertheless a non-metallic enterprise is a capital intensive undertaking. Fortunately for the potential investor, the price structure of most of these industries is less volatile and the level of consumption is somewhat more predictable than for the metal minerals. Costs and profit margins can be anticipated with somewhat greater confidence for a new project to produce, say, barite, phosphate rock or talc than for a comparable venture to produce copper, nickel or zinc.

Several factors make the outlook for non-metallic minerals more readily definable than for metallic commodities. One is the relative abundance of world resources — this reduces anxiety about possible shortages, something that regularly crops up in connection with metals. Another is the low level of prices for non-metallic products. Consumers have few incentives to seek less expensive substitutes. A third is that most non-metallic commodities are closely tied to clearly identifiable markets. Thus phosphates, potash and to a lesser extent sulphur are heavily dependent on agriculture. Asbestos and gypsum demand arises primarily from construction. Barite is largely linked to oil-drilling activity.

Later in this chapter brief descriptions are provided of these and other major non-metallic minerals. Because consumption statistics are not compiled on a global basis for many non-metallic minerals, world production data are cited. These constitute effective measurements of demand trends over an extended period since production must eventually align with the level of consumption. The bulk nature and low value of non-metallic products discourages the kind of inventory stocking and de-stocking that occurs in higher value products.

Production data for the centrally-planned countries, as estimated by the U.S. Bureau of Mines, are included in the totals. Even though the figures are not official statistics, the Bureau's estimates provide a valid impression of the order of magnitude of output in nations with Socialist governments. Only limited trade in non-metallic minerals is carried on between market-economy and centrally-planned countries (Soviet Union exports of asbestos to some Western European nations are a possible exception). Undoubtedly the absence of such trade reflects the widespread existence of non-metallic mineral deposits in both the market-economy and centrally-planned nations.

Non-Metallics have Fared Better than Metals since 1973

Non-metallic minerals have outperformed metallic minerals in the turbulent economic environment that has prevailed since 1973. This is true both with respect to the volume of production and in the ability to offset the ravages of inflation through compensating price changes.

This is demonstrated by comparing production of 12 non-metallic mineral industries with production of the 12 principal metal mining industries. Between 1973 and 1985, world production of five non-metallic minerals rose by more than 30% — gypsum, phosphate rock, potash, soda ash, and talc. In the same period only chromium and magnesium among the metals experienced world production increases of as much as 30%. Of the 12 non-metallic industries only two — fluorspar and boron — failed to record production gains in 1985 as against 1973. During this same period five metal mining industries — bauxite, iron ore, lead, manganese ore and tin — either experienced unchanged output or actually declined in volume. The data are presented in Chart 10.

An equally striking contrast took place in price behaviour of the two mineral groups during the 1973-85 period. This is shown in Tables 8 and 9 covering prices in the United States for seven

CHART 10. CHANGES IN WORLD PRODUCTION OF LEADING MINERALS SINCE ONSET OF ENERGY CRISIS
Gains or Losses Expressed in Percentages Between 1973 and 1985

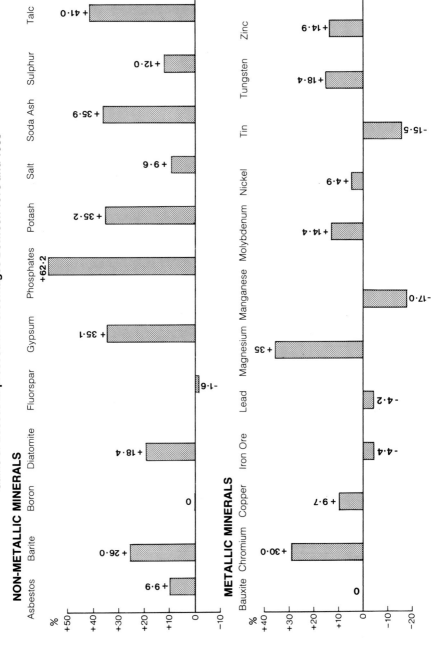

144

non-metallic and seven metallic minerals. Some commodities (asbestos, fluorspar, soda ash and talc among the non-metallics and chrome, iron, manganese and tungsten ores among the metals) are not included because price data for them are affected by variations in quality, physical characteristics, and other factors. However, even though less consistent, the price trends for the omitted commodities are essentially similar to the trends for the items covered.

Meaningful price data for non-metallic minerals are not available on a worldwide basis. The substantial costs involved in transporting low-value commodities such as non-metallic minerals cause wide price differentials among the various markets. The prices used in the comparison are the annual averages prevailing in the United States as published by the U.S. Bureau of Mines. These are considered representative prices as the United States is the largest consumer and a major producer of non-metallic minerals.

Although prices of all 14 minerals covered in the tabulation rose between 1973 and 1985, the extent of the rise differed widely. As a yardstick of inflation, the table includes the U.S. Government's Gross National Product Deflator Price Index, based on 1982 equalling 100. The index stood at 49.5 in 1973 and at 111.7 in 1985 — an increase of 125.7%.

Therefore, to the extent that the price of a given mineral rose by less than 125.7% between 1973 and 1985, that industry had not offset the effect of inflation. If the price rose by more than 125.7%, then inflation had been offset and the producers of that mineral had presumably been more likely to have experienced a favourable return on investment.

Of the seven non-metallic minerals covered in Table 8, five had gains of more than 125.7%. Only gypsum, up 98.8%, and barite, up 85.2%, failed to match inflation over the 13 year span.

The record for the metals is quite different. Only in the case of tin, with a rise of 161.8% between 1973 and 1985, did the price outpace inflation. As discussed in Chapter 6, that gain was subsequently wiped out by the collapse of the International Tin Council's programme for price stabilization. Prices of the other six metals increased less than 100% during this period and thus they lost ground

145

TABLE 8: U.S. PRICES FOR NON-METALLIC MINERALS 1973-85

Year	U.S. Gross National Product Deflator Price Index 1982 = 100	Barite $	Boron $	Diatomite $	Gypsum $	Phosphate Rock $	Salt $	Sulphur $
1973	49·5	16·66	88·18	65·04	4·60	6·24	6·82	17·56
1974	54·04	16·77	108·03	83·77	4·86	12·10	7·87	28·42
1975	59·3	17·70	115·74	88·18	5·04	25·35	9·85	44·91
1976	63·1	25·63	121·25	95·90	5·51	21·26	8·62	45·72
1977	67·3	22·33	130·07	109·13	6·12	17·39	9·85	44·38
1978	72·2	22·71	141·09	122·36	6·87	18·56	11·13	45·17
1979	78·6	28·08	184·08	138·89	7·53	20·04	11·03	55·75
1980	85·7	32·39	186·28	160·94	9·18	22·78	16·15	89·06
1981	94·0	39·64	205·03	180·78	9·40	26·63	15·17	111·48
1982	100·0	41·53	221·56	194·00	9·33	25·52	15·31	108·27
1983	103·8	42·69	221·56	203·93	8·68	23·97	14·80	87·24
1984	108·1	36·19	229·28	212·74	8·75	23·99	15·19	94·31
1985	111·7	30·86	229·28	230·38	9·15	23·50	15·43	104·68
Change 1973-85	+125·7%	+85·2%	+160·0%	+254·1%	+98·8%	+176·6%	+126·3%	+486·1%

All prices are in $U.S. per ton of material, f.o.b. shipping point.

Source: U.S. Bureau of Mines for prices. GNP Deflator Index as reported by American Bureau of Metal Statistics.

to inflation. Prices of two metals — copper and lead — rose by less than 20% between 1973 and 1985, resulting in an extreme adverse impact of rising costs. In some interim years copper and lead had benefited from temporary price peaks.

Because of low prices and great bulk, non-metallic minerals have not proved of major interest to traders or speculators. No non-metallic minerals are traded on commodity exchanges. The high proportion of total delivered value represented by transportation makes it unattractive to move these materials from point of production to an intermediate point for warehousing and then on to an ultimate consuming destination. Moreover, exchanges would find problems inherent in grading and inspecting these commodities.

Nevertheless, prices of non-metallics do respond to factors of costs, supply and demand as will be shown in the comments regarding the 12 individual commodities. Most commercial transactions are negotiated directly between producers and consumers. In addition to the chemical analysis of the product physical characteristics are of great significance if not of overriding importance in many cases. For many products shipments are prepared to meet specific requirements of individual customers. Visual inspection or special testing procedures are required for some non-metallics. Thus, once a relationship has been established between a given supplier and a given consumer, there is a tendency to enter into long-term contracts.

Relatively few sales of non-metallic minerals are made on the basis of spot transactions for a single lot of material, unlike the situation that is prevalent to a considerable extent in the metal markets.

In the 12 non-metallic mineral industries described, production is largely from developed market-economy or centrally-planned nations. The developing countries undoubtedly have adequate resources of many of these materials but they have been slow to undertake production because of limited home markets and high transport costs that would erode a large share of foreign exchange earnings arising from exports.

Undoubtedly this situation will gradually change as developing countries embark on industrialization and as they acquire growing expertise through transfer of technology. Furthermore, environmen-

TABLE 9: U.S. PRICES FOR NON-FERROUS METALS 1973-85

Year	U.S. Gross National Product Deflator Price Index 1982 = 100	Aluminium $	Copper $	Lead $	Molyb- denum $	Nickel $	Tin $	Zinc $
1973	49·5	573	1,312	359	4,233	3,373	5,018	455
1974	54·0	948	1,700	496	4,938	3,836	8,737	793
1975	59·3	772	1,422	473	6,041	4,475	7,491	859
1976	63·1	903	1,534	509	7,187	4,850	8,373	815
1977	67·3	1,058	1,475	677	8,862	4,783	11,786	758
1978	72·2	1,124	1,466	743	10,714	4,586	13,880	653
1979	78·6	1,565	2,033	1,162	13,382	5,313	16,622	822
1980	85·7	1,675	2,233	935	20,635	7,518	18,651	825
1981	94·0	1,323	1,856	805	14,109	5,886	16,160	982
1982	100·0	1,036	1,605	562	9,039	4,933	14,416	848
1983	103·8	1,499	1,687	478	8,025	4,850	14,436	912
1984	108·1	1,347	1,472	564	7,848	4,894	13,757	1,071
1985	111·7	1,014	1,475	419	6,944	5,026	13,139	892
Change 1973-85	+125·7%	+77·0%	+12·4%	+16·7%	+64·0%	+49·0%	+161·8%	+96·0%

All prices are in $U.S. per ton as reported by the U.S. Bureau of Mines.

148

tal restrictions and gradual depletion of high-grade resources will work towards reducing the market share of production from the developed countries. But the key word is gradual. In non-metallics a developing country can hardly expect the kind of rapid expansion that has taken place in, say, the production of bauxite in Guinea or of gold in Brazil or of copper in Chile.

To provide a bird's eye view of the significant role that non-metallics play in modern society, the following capsule descriptions of 12 representative non-metallic minerals deal with some important factors in consumption, production, and price.

Asbestos — Important markets for asbestos are: asbestos-cement pipe used for water distribution systems; asbestos-cement products used in building construction; roofing products; asbestos-vinyl or asbestos-asphalt floor tile; brake linings for automotive vehicles; and asbestos textiles used in fireproof clothing and theatre curtains. Demand for these purposes had risen consistently for many years through the early seventies. After 1970 increasing concern over health effects from exposure to asbestos caused restrictions to be imposed on its use in certain applications by industrialized countries. This was offset by continuing expansion of consumption in developing countries and in the centrally-planned nations, resulting in record use in 1979. In the eighties severe drops in consumption in the United States and Western Europe have reduced the overall size of the world asbestos market. In 1985 more than 50% of world output came from the Soviet Union, and about 22.5% from Canada. South Africa and Zimbabwe are other significant sources. In recent years the Government of the Province of Quebec has acquired ownership of a substantial share of the Canadian industry. After rising sharply between 1973 and 1977 to offset cost increases resulting from inflation, prices have since moved within a relatively narrow range despite continued increases in costs.

Barite — This mineral has one major market — for use as a weighting medium in the drilling of oil and gas wells. In the United States

TABLE 10: WORLD PRODUCTION OF SOME IMPORTANT NON-METALLIC MINERALS 1973-85

(000's of tons)

Year	Asbestos	Barite	Boron*	Diatomite	Fluorspar	Gypsum	Phosphate	Potash	Salt	Soda Ash	Sulphur	Talc
1973	4,186	4,486	995	1,287	4,807	61,534	98,010	21,147	154,661	21,368	48,198	5,404
1974	4,157	4,635	954	1,392	4,944	61,421	110,787	23,794	166,231	22,437	51,153	5,701
1975	4,139	4,916	1,030	1,327	4,612	59,221	107,557	24,739	161,668	23,365	50,678	4,885
1976	4,767	5,203	1,088	1,335	4,427	66,124	107,304	24,386	168,125	24,474	50,908	5,267
1977	4,793	5,799	1,266	1,305	4,520	74,512	115,948	25,252	169,911	25,440	52,383	5,625
1978	4,693	6,814	1,342	1,307	4,737	77,800	125,000	26,113	163,753	27,210	52,138	6,397
1979	4,906	6,677	975	1,367	4,681	80,367	132,000	25,768	173,371	28,188	53,227	6,876
1980	4,699	7,532	993	1,342	4,888	78,300	139,000	27,857	168,901	28,349	54,920	7,530
1981	4,337	8,197	956	1,322	4,839	76,157	138,000	27,080	171,393	28,100	53,350	7,217
1982	4,080	7,491	820	1,300	4,334	71,641	122,000	24,664	165,065	27,549	50,776	6,890
1983	4,157	5,522	936	1,306	4,407	77,859	135,000	28,619	163,032	29,030	50,472	6,852
1984	4,338	5,727	980	1,511	4,600	81,921	150,571	28,638	167,951	29,030	51,884	7,228
1985	4,600	5,652	989	1,524	4,727	83,144	159,000	28,600	169,555	29,030	54,000	7,620

Source: U.S. Bureau of Mines. 1985 figures are preliminary.

* Boron oxide content of material produced.

currently this single use accounts for more than 95% of total consumption. Small amounts are used by the chemical, paint and glass industries and in medical applications. The sharp rise in exploration for oil and gas following the energy crisis of 1973-74 caused an increase of 83% in world barite production between 1973 and 1981. The subsequent easing in oil prices has since reduced drilling activity with a consequent shrinkage in barite sales. Nevertheless tonnages mined in 1985 were 26% greater than in 1973. Barite deposits occur in many countries. The People's Republic of China is currently ranked as the largest producer, with an output in 1985 estimated at close to 19% of the world total. The United States accounts for 13% of current supply. The Soviet Union, Mexico, Morocco, India and Germany F.R. each contribute 4 to 8% of the world total. Prices of barite rose steadily through 1982 but have since weakened as sales volume has diminished.

Boron Minerals — The glass and ceramic industries constitute the largest use of boron minerals, with glass fibres being the specific application taking the greatest tonnage — both for insulation and textile fibreglass. Borosilicate glass can withstand severe temperature changes and has wide application in laboratory ware, cooking utensils and automotive headlights. Other significant uses are in soaps and detergents, in metallurgy as a fluxing material, and as a fire retardant. The United States is by far the largest producer of boron minerals, accounting for 58% of the 1985 world total. Turkey, with 34% of the total, is the other significant source. The price for boron minerals, f.o.b. mine sources in the United States, has risen in line with the effects of inflation on production costs. Between 40 and 50% of U.S. mine production is sold in export markets. Hence the U.S. price obviously is representative of the world market.

Diatomite — Also known as diatomaceous earth and kieselguhr, this mineral has wide applications as a filtering medium for the separation of suspended solids in liquids. It is required by a wide range of industries, including food and food processing, chemical, beverage, building materials, pharmaceuticals, and water treatment. The other major use of diatomite is as a filler material employed in the paint, paper, pesticide, fertilizer and building materials fields. This broad diversity of markets has resulted in an uncommon degree of stability in demand for diatomite — which has been relatively constant during the period of violent economic change since 1973. The United States has consistently produced between 40 and 45% of the world total output in recent years. In addition to supplying domestic demand, U.S. diatomite producers export about one-fifth of their output to Japan, Canada, the United Kingdom and other countries. The second largest producer is the Soviet Union, accounting for about 15% of world total. Available data indicate that the Soviets are neither exporters nor importers of diatomite. France, Denmark, and the Federal Republic of Germany account for most of the balance of production among the market-economy nations. Diatomite prices have more than kept pace with inflation in the United States.

Fluorspar — Demand for fluorspar arises largely from the chemical, steel and aluminium industries with small amounts also being used in ceramics, glass and pottery. Fluorspar is marketed in three grades — acid-grade, which is taken by the chemical and aluminium industries; metallurgical grade, which is used by the steel industry; and ceramic grade required for ceramics, glass and pottery. Each of these grades is produced to specifications related to calcium fluoride, silica, and other constituents. Among the market-economy countries Mexico is the largest producer, accounting for 15% of the world total. South Africa, France, Thailand, the United Kingdom, and Spain each account for between 4 and 6% of world supply. Among the centrally-planned countries Mongolia with an estimated 16% of the total is the largest producer. The Soviet Union and China are also substantial fluorspar miners. Reflecting problems in the steel and aluminium industries, fluorspar is one of only two non-metallic minerals among the 12 under review that failed to expand markets between 1973 and 1985. Prices have, nevertheless, risen in line with inflationary trends but price competition is at times keen with material being offered on occasions at discounts from the published quotations.

Gypsum — The great increase in gypsum consumption since 1950 has been primarily due to the development of gypsum wallboard. This has become the preferred construction material for apartment and commercial structures worldwide. More than two-thirds of gypsum consumption is now for this purpose but the mineral also has significant applications as a retarder for cement in the setting of concrete, as a soil neutralizer in the agricultural industry, in the production of industrial plaster, and as a filler. With its ready availability and low price, gypsum demand will vary directly with the level of construction activity. Gypsum, the most common of the naturally occurring sulphate minerals, is widely distributed. The United States accounts for about 15% of world production and Canada about 10%. France, Spain, Iran, Japan, and the Soviet Union each produce more than 5% of the total and many other countries are significant producers. Despite this pattern of distribution and low price, substantial tonnages of gypsum are shipped between countries when low-cost ocean freight rates are available for cargoes shipped to large centres of population. For example, the United States imports large quantities from Canada at eastern seaboard points that are relatively remote from domestic deposits. The price has risen slowly to reflect inflationary cost increases. Were prices to rise substantially, significant quantities of by-product gypsum could be recovered from phosphate rock processing, chemical operations, and flue gas desulphurization plants.

Phosphate Rock — The preponderant use of phosphate rock is in the production of fertilizers for agriculture but there are other uses in detergents, cleaners, water treatment, animal feeds, dentifrices, and food products such as baking powders. Because phosphorous is not usually abundant in soil and is removed by crop and natural losses, phosphate fertilizer application to most soils is essential. This has caused a steady increase in global consumption of phosphate rock as world population and food consumption has increased. Long the world's largest producer, the United States currently mines over 30% of the total, with the Soviet Union accounting for 20%, Morocco about 15% and China slightly less than 10%. Tunisia, Jordan, Israel, and the Pacific Ocean island of Nauru are other significant sources. Environmental problems may inhibit further increases in United States production, but ample supplies elsewhere indicate consumption needs will be met. Phosphate rock prices rose sharply in the mid-seventies when Moroccan producers undertook an effort to parallel the oil price rise instituted by OPEC. Prices subsequently weakened as a consequence of competition, but rising costs and strong demand again brought about price increases in 1979 and 1980. The advent of the subsequent recession caused price weakness in 1982 and 1983. To an extent, therefore, phosphate prices have been more volatile than for most other non-metallics. Despite fluctuations, however, phosphate rock prices over the years have fully compensated for the effect of inflation on costs.

Potash — Like phosphate rock, the predominant use of potash is for agricultural fertilizers with consumption heaviest in the developed nations where farmers have traditionally used fertilizers intensively. Consumption has increased substantially, if to a somewhat lesser extent than consumption of phosphate rock. Some potash is used in the manufacture of gypsum wallboard. Potassium hydroxide has end uses in soaps and detergents, glass and ceramics, chemical dyes and drugs. In the aggregate, however, the non-fertilizer uses account for only slightly more than 5% of potash consumption. The Soviet Union is believed to produce about one-third of total potash output, followed by Canada with almost one-quarter. The other large producers are Germany D.R., Germany F.R., France, the United States and Israel. Production of potash in the developing nations is at present quite limited, but indicated resources in Brazil, Thailand, Tunisia and Chile have attracted attention as possible large-scale sources. Although prices quoted for potash have risen substantially since the early seventies, increased operating costs in the United States have caused U.S. production to decline by about 40% since 1973, while output in other countries — notably Canada — has risen.

Salt — The expression 'salt of the earth' to connote excellence in an individual measures the importance mankind has long ascribed to this

non-metallic mineral, an essential nutrient for the existence of life —
even though excess quantities may be harmful. The chemical industry
is today the largest consumer of salt. It is also used in food,
agriculture, water treatment and, where cold climates prevail, for
de-icing of highways. As measured by recorded world production,
consumption is on the whole quite stable, with minor fluctuations in
line with broad economic trends. Production of salt includes a
substantial amount recovered from brine through solution mining,
large amounts recovered through extraction of rock salt by traditional mining methods, and a significant quantity recovered by solar
or mechanical evaporation of seawater. A minor amount of salt is
also recovered in the conversion of saline water into fresh water.
Almost every nation is a producer of salt but the dominant sources
are the United States (18%), the Soviet Union and China (each about
10%), Germany F.R. (6%) and Canada, the United Kingdom, India,
France, Australia and Mexico (about 5% each). Despite this
widespread distribution of production, a surprising amount of
international commerce takes place in the commodity — Japan, for
example, imports millions of tons annually from Australia and
Mexico rather than attempting to recover salt from seawater which
would involve extensive input of energy. Prices for salt vary widely
depending on whether they are for rock salt, salt in brine, solar salt,
or other types. Nevertheless, prices tend to move more or less in
concert with cost factors as the principal determinant. The prices
shown in the tabulation are for rock salt.

Soda Ash. — This important compound is used primarily in the glass
industry and to a lesser extent in chemicals, soaps and detergents,
water treatment, and in the pulp and paper industry — although the
latter is a far larger consumer of the related compound, sodium
sulphate. World production of soda ash has been steadily increasing
in response chiefly to the rising demand for glass from the construction, automobile, and container industries. With respect to the latter,
the recent development of plastic containers to replace glass may
result in some loss of market. Soda ash production is categorized as
coming from natural sources, such as the mineral trona or natural

155

brines, or from synthetic sources, meaning chemical recovery by one of several processes, of which the best known is the Solvay process which uses salt and limestone as raw materials. Most of the output in the United States, the largest soda ash producer with 26% of the world total, is from trona deposits in Wyoming and natural brines in California. Elsewhere, however, production is largely of synthetic soda ash. The Soviet Union (16·5%), China (6%), France, Bulgaria, the United Kingdom, Japan and Romania are the other large suppliers. Reflecting the heavy energy input in synthetic production, prices rose steadily between 1973 and 1980, but have since weakened as fuel prices have softened.

Sulphur. — Sulphuric acid, a key material for the chemical industry, accounts for all but 15% of the consumption of sulphur. Fertilizers in turn represent the largest single field for which sulphuric acid is an essential raw material. However, plastic and synthetic products, paper products, paints, the production of non-ferrous metals, explosives, petroleum refining, and iron and steel are other major industries that require sulphuric acid in large quantities. As a consequence, sulphuric acid consumption is regarded as a significant index of a nation's industrial development. Sulphur production is diverse. Elemental sulphur is produced both from deposits that are exploited chiefly for their sulphur content and from natural gas and petroleum refining. However, some sulphur is produced directly as sulphuric acid recovered from non-ferrous smelter gases and from the roasting of pyrites. Because increased quantities of sulphur and sulphuric acid are being recovered as a by-product of natural gas, oil, and non-ferrous metal production (in considerable measure due to environmental regulations), the share of the market supplied by companies operating natural sulphur deposits has tended to diminish in recent years. Production of sulphur from all sources is widely distributed. The Soviet Union and the United States each produce approximately 19% of the world's supply, followed by Canada (13%), Poland (10%) and Japan and China (each 5%). Prices, greatly depressed in the early seventies, have since recovered substantially.

Talc. — This designation covers a group of versatile soft non-metallic minerals, including pure talc itself, soapstone, steatite, and pyrophyllite. The largest present uses are in the ceramic and paint industries, with substantial demand also from the roofing, paper, refractory, cosmetic and rubber industries. A significant long-term potential is believed to lie in the plastics industries. Talc may find a market as an economic filler to enhance the strength and other properties of lighter-weight fibre-reinforced plastics, now being studied as replacement for structural steel parts in vehicles. Production of talc minerals is widely distributed around the world, the largest producer being Japan, with 21% of the world total in 1985 (primarily of the mineral pyrophyllite). The United States production, 14% of the total, ranked next. China accounts for about 12%. Finland, the Republic of Korea, France and Brazil are other significant producers. Italy is a major source of high-quality block talc. Prices of the different grades of talc vary greatly. Prices have risen sharply, considerably outpacing inflation.

These necessarily brief descriptions only provide an overview of some significant trends in the development of 12 widely differing industries. However, they do provide support for the belief that, with one or two exceptions, the non-metallics are unlikely to experience the problems of major market loss through substitution or of widely fluctuating prices in times of economic adversity.

Indeed, for most non-metallic minerals continued market expansion closely linked to population trends and growth in the overall economy seems probable.

CHAPTER EIGHT

Minerals Import Dependency
and National Security

Access to Raw Material Supplies is a Military Concern

"An army marches on its stomach", Napoleon once observed. Today armies consume much more than food. Within the past hundred years the development of mechanized warfare has brought with it requirements for huge quantities of a myriad assortment of minerals.

Confronted with the task of ensuring national security, military leaders have developed a bewildering array of modern weapons and munitions. Commodities virtually unknown to the general public have become critically important as scientists devise ever more sophisticated arms.

The distribution of minerals resources around the world differs widely from the geographical pattern of consumption. So governments of the great powers worry about access to mineral raw materials. Not only are they important in wartime, their availability is essential to prosperity in peacetime.

The problem is particularly acute for countries with large populations contained within relatively small territorial areas. These countries typically have limited mineral production, in many cases the consequence of past intensive exploitation of their original resources. Heavily dependent on other nations, most of their mineral needs are now transported over long sealanes which are highly vulnerable in wartime.

Indeed, many historians and geo-politicians believe that the two World Wars in this century were caused by the desire of Germany on both occasions and Japan on the second to annex territories producing raw material resources which they lacked. Their rulers felt disadvantaged in relation to the other major industrial powers. Prior to both wars Britain and France ruled over vast colonial empires with abundant and diversified resources. The United States and Russia were enormous countries producing a great variety of raw materials. To compete, the Germans and the Japanese sought similar resource assets.

Despite early military successes and territorial gains, victory was eventually denied the Germans and the Japanese. What defeated them were naval blockades that cut off access to essential overseas supplies. Shortages of oil and minerals hampered their production of weapons and munitions. In the long run these shortages helped cause military defeat.

It is ironic that, having lost the wars, both Germany and Japan appear to have won the peace. The raw materials they could not secure in wartime are now abundantly available to them. Countries of the developing world are anxious to broaden markets for their mineral exports. Coupled with the interest of the Germans and the Japanese in ensuring long-term access, this has led to sales arrangements on terms and at prices which at least match the availability of minerals to the United States and the Soviet Union from their domestic resources and to the United Kingdom and France from their former colonial possessions.

With ample raw materials assured, industrial production and standards of living in Germany and Japan have risen more rapidly than in the nations that gained the military victory in World War II.

Ownership or control over raw material sources no longer appears to confer special peacetime economic advantages. Countries without indigenous mining industries can readily obtain needed mineral raw materials for their manufacturing requirements at the lowest available costs. These may be lower than costs incurred by competitive manufacturers in countries with their own mineral enterprises where high-cost operations are being supported for social reasons.

If permanent peace were assured, perhaps the issue of control over mineral supplies as an instrument of national policy could be disregarded. But in a troubled world permanent peace is not assured. And so leaders of governments, aware of the vital role that access to

TABLE 11: ASSESSMENT OF NATIONAL MINERAL SELF-SUFFICIENCY OR IMPORT DEPENDENCE

Country	Bauxite	Chromite	Copper	Iron Ore	Lead	Manganese	Nickel	Phosphate	Potash	Tin	Zinc	Aggregate
Australia	1	5	2	1	1	1	1	5	6	2	1	26
Brazil	2	4	4	1	4	1	1	4	6	1	4	32
Canada	6	6	1	1	1	6	1	6	1	3*	1	33
France	4	6	6	4	4	6	6	6	2	6	4	54
Germany F.R.	6	6	6	5	5	6	6	6	2	6	5	59
Great Britain	6	6	6	5	5	6	6	6	4	4	5	59
India	3	2	4	2	4	1	6	4	6	6	4	42
Italy	5	6	5	6	5	5	6	6	4	6	5	60
Japan	6	5	5	5	5	5	6	6	4	6	5	58
South Africa	6	1	2	1	2	1	3	2	6	3	2	29
United States	5	6	4	4	3	6	5	1	4	6	4	48

The numbers in this tabulation are based as follows:

1 indicates the country is a major mine producer and exporter
2 indicates major mine production and some exports
3 indicates mine production is adequate for basic self-sufficiency
4 indicates significant mine production with some import dependence
5 indicates modest mine production and heavy import dependence
6 indicates little or no mine production and substantially entire import dependence.

Table prepared using data contained in *U.S. Bureau of Mines Yearbook, Volume III, International*, giving statistics on production, exports and imports of individual countries for 1983.

* Based on new project expected to make Canada self-sufficient.

raw material supplies played in both World Wars, worry about minerals availability.

The centrally-planned countries differ radically from the market-economy nations in their approach to this problem. The former group — particularly the Soviet Union and the People's Republic of China — have unmistakably clear policies. The centrally-planned economy concept assumes rigid control of all aspects of production and consumption, with minimal dependence on foreign trade. These countries believe in self-sufficiency where at all possible, regardless of cost. They do not wish to rely on other nations for minerals or, for that matter, for any other commodity. They particularly wish to avoid dependence on sources that involve overseas shipments. The state of their mineral industries and the degree of their import dependence is the subject of the next chapter.

The market-economy countries, with some exceptions, concentrate on producing those minerals that meet competitive standards in the international market-place. They look to imports to supply what they cannot economically mine themselves. This can be demonstrated by examining the posture of 11 important trading nations. Of these, six are countries with large and diversified mining industries. The other five are countries with small land areas, large populations and relatively limited remaining mineral resources.

In the first group are Australia, Brazil, Canada, India, and the United States. All control extensive territory within their national boundaries. South Africa, although its land area is smaller, is classed with the first group because of the unusually diverse and abundant deposits of minerals within its boundaries.

The second group consists of France, Germany F.R., Great Britain, Italy and Japan. Small in area and with large populations, all five have already drawn heavily upon their original mineral endowment. Few opportunities exist for them to expand domestic mineral supplies on a competitive basis. Should circumstances require them to reduce imports, these countries would have to turn to marginal, high-cost, low-grade mineral resources.

While the six countries in the first group have large mining industries, none is entirely self-sufficient. Table 11 covers both

161

groups and indicates a rough approximation of each country's degree of mineral import dependence.

Six categories have been identified to indicate relative self-sufficiency or import dependence. A number has been assigned to each category. The lower the number, the higher the degree of self-sufficiency. The position of each country is appraised in respect of each of the 11 key minerals cited in Chapter 1 — bauxite, chromite, copper, iron ore, lead, manganese ore, nickel, phosphates, potash, tin and zinc. Of course, many other minerals are vital to military and essential civilian production but these 11 are the bulk materials without which national survival would be impossible in war and standards of living would collapse in peace.

The numbers shown in the table are based on statistics of production, imports, and exports in recent years. Over time, of course, a country's position is subject to change as old mines close or new mines are opened.

A century ago Great Britain's rating on iron ore and copper would have been quite different from today. South Africa's position in lead and zinc is of recent origin; 30 years ago it was an importer of both. Brazil is a relatively new source of bauxite and tin, while — as pointed out in Chapter 2 — Australia has only emerged as a major factor in iron ore, bauxite, manganese and nickel since the mid-fifties. The United States has been losing ground as a producer of copper, iron ore, potash and zinc. Canada's rating on tin is based on the expectation that a new mine in Nova Scotia, which started up in 1985, may make it substantially self-sufficient for this metal. A few years ago Canada's tin rating would have been six rather than three.

Some of the present ratings involve an exercise of judgement. Should the extremely modest copper production of Germany F.R., France, Great Britain and Italy entitle them to a rating of five rather than six? Considering the large amount of copper these four countries consume, it was felt a six rating (virtual total import dependence) was a more accurate appraisal.

The number of marginal situations is small. The aggregates shown in the table are believed to be reasonably representative of each country's comparative ranking. On the basis of the figures Italy,

Great Britain, Japan and Germany F.R. are all extremely import-dependent. Australia is ranked as the most nearly self-sufficient, followed by South Africa, Brazil and Canada. India, the United States and France constitute a middle group. No single market-economy country is a producer of all 11 minerals — Australia has no potash production currently and is heavily dependent on imports for phosphate and chromite.

To cope with problems of import dependence, countries have adopted different approaches. Moreover, within any one country, the approach adopted may differ at different times. New priorities arise as political or economic circumstances evolve. At one time the emphasis may be on military problems created by import dependence; at other times the key issue may be the nation's trade balance; at still another time economic development and dealing with high unemployment rates may be the paramount objective; or perhaps the shadow of substantial government deficits may override all other considerations.

Thus, many strategies have been tried. These include measures to stimulate domestic mine production; to encourage maximum recycling of minerals through reprocessing of wastes; to develop more effective ways to use minerals, thereby conserving available supplies; or to substitute other commodities for those where import dependence is greatest. An approach widely supported in some countries is the creation of stockpiles to be used only in times of emergency — essentially Joseph's plan to assist Pharaoh.

Entire books have been written covering each of these courses of action. They are briefly summarized as follows.

Stimulating Domestic Mine Production
The tradition of protecting domestic producers of agricultural commodities is widespread among the major consuming powers. Price supports, quotas and protective tariffs on farm products exist in profusion among nations that profess adherence to the ideology of free trade. These measures to insulate their local farmers from the rigours of international competition have been devised by politicians

who are only too keenly aware of the massive voting strength of the agricultural sectors of their countries.

The mineral industries do not rate equal attention from legislators or administrators among the principal consuming countries of the market-economy world. This may not be entirely unrelated to the mineral industry's limited voting strength. For the most part current mineral production in the industrialized countries comes from enterprises that can survive in a worldwide market-place. There are some instances of tariffs, quotas and other protective measures for minerals but these are more prevalent as means to assist mineral processing industries rather than miners. Where protection for processors exists, as in the case of Japan, the nation's reliance on imports of mine products is not altered.

In some cases protection appears to be motivated more by balance of trade considerations than by a desire to assist the mineral industry. This appears to be true of the measures taken by India and Brazil to promote indigenous productions of copper, lead and zinc. Both these countries have ambitious plans for industrialization. Both were hard hit by the steep rise in oil prices, which created great balance-of-payments problems, beginning in 1974.

Since both countries have substantial reserves of base metals in unexploited low-grade deposits, they embarked in the early seventies on programmes to increase their domestic base metal mine production thus conserving foreign exchange while providing raw materials for their burgeoning industries. Domestic miners have been given preferred access to the domestic market through licensing of imports, currency restrictions that add to the cost of imports, and investment of government funds in public sector mining companies.

In other countries special tax inducements are offered to the mining industry. These include depletion allowances for miners or tax exemption during the first years of production. Some governments provide low-cost loans to mining enterprises. Governments may absorb the cost of infrastructure required for new mining projects such as transportation, power supply or even housing for workers. In some cases governments have offered special assistance to develop new mining projects or re-open old mines in areas of high

164

unemployment. Examples include lead-zinc operations in Sardinia, Italy and Yukon, Canada and a copper project in Michigan, U.S.A.

Among the developing countries that depend on mineral exports to provide foreign exchange as well as industrial employment, public sector companies are given financial assistance to offset operating losses in periods of low mineral prices. The Zambian copper industry and the Bolivian tin industry are typical examples. The Philippine Government guaranteed a floor price to its private sector copper miners in 1983 and 1984, thereby maintaining production.

In wartime, more direct measures may be instituted to stimulate domestic production of minerals as a hedge against possible interruption of imports. For example, prior to World War II the United States had no production of chromite and only limited production of manganese. Fears arose that overseas supplies of both minerals could be drastically reduced or possibly entirely interrupted. Even before the country became directly involved in the War, government corporations began investing large sums to develop and equip marginal low-grade domestic deposits of both minerals. Significant production was attained by 1943. However, the domestic products were of inferior quality. Meanwhile, U.S. imports from South Africa, India, Brazil and even the Soviet Union had been maintained and these products were preferred by consumers. When war ended most of the domestic production was still in stockpile. Thus a programme that had been costly both in terms of capital and manpower proved to be an insurance against events that might but did not occur.

These examples are the exceptions. On the whole, the consuming countries of the market-economy sector have resisted pressure to stimulate non-economic minerals production in peacetime. They are content to let market forces determine where minerals are produced.

Encouraging Recycling

A favourite approach for nations with limited mineral resources of their own is to try to recover large quantities of minerals through recycling of scrap. Technological progress in the collection, handling and processing of scrap has led to increased production of secondary

165

materials in recent years. The prospects for further progress are good. Because minerals are inorganic and resist deterioration they lend themselves to recycling.

For example, copper's enduring qualities are widely recognized. Copper artefacts of ancient civilizations date back to the second or third millenium before the Christian Era. Estimates have been made that 90% of all copper consumed is potentially available for recycling. However, recycling occurs only when the product in which it is contained has become obsolete. Buildings with copper roofs, copper plumbing or copper hardware may remain in use for centuries.

Comparisons are sometimes made between the quantity of copper salvaged from scrap and the quantity of copper entering into current consumption. This is neither a good measure of the efficiency of the recycling industry nor of the potential quantities available for current secondary production. The comparisons are meaningless because of the wide range in the useful life-cycle of copper-containing articles. This is probably upwards of 50 years, considering the large amounts of copper consumed in the utility and construction industries. Therefore, a more correct comparison would be between the 1985 secondary production of copper and the 1935 rate of consumption.

In some quarters unrealistic expectations are held about recycling. Some environmentalists apparently assume all mineral-containing products can be recycled. But certain applications do not lend themselves to recycling, including most non-metallic minerals and those metals used in chemical applications or as coatings, desulphurizing and deoxidizing agents, pigments, and plastic stabilizers.

For many countries, statistical information on minerals recycling is fragmentary. Accurate reporting is difficult because of the diverse ways in which scrap originates, is collected, and is processed. Three broad classifications of scrap can be identified: home scrap, new scrap, and old scrap.

Home scrap is material re-circulated within a single industrial operation. In any metallurgical plant a substantial share of the throughput undergoes such re-circulation. Statistics covering home scrap volumes are rarely reported to outsiders. Since processing of home scrap is basically a means to attain maximum recovery from the raw material input of a plant, the absence of published statistics on home scrap is not a significant omission. The relevant statistical information is the final output of a given operation in relation to its intake of raw materials.

New scrap is material generated in the process of fabricating or manufacturing which the fabricator or manufacturer either returns to the plant that supplied his raw materials or sells to a scrap collector, who then makes arrangements for reprocessing. Statistics are published about the volumes of new scrap generated or processed because they frequently involve arms-length transactions between separate parties. However, new scrap does not really represent an addition to a country's available supply. If a country is 100% import dependent for primary supplies of a particular mineral and if imports of that mineral cease, the generation of new scrap will also cease in time.

Old scrap is a positive addition to a nation's raw material supply. It consists of material salvaged from demolished buildings, abandoned power and railway lines, replaced industrial machinery, or discarded vehicles — including ships, railway equipment, aircraft, trucks, buses and cars. Old scrap constitutes a true substitute for imports.

Aware of this, many industrial nations with inadequate mineral production have taken steps to prohibit or severely limit the export of scrap. Such steps constitute barriers to international commerce as real as import limitations. Relatively little attention is paid to impediments to scrap exports in multilateral trade negotiations. Politicians who consider themselves free traders apparently do not recognize any inconsistency in advocating scrap export restrictions.

How large a share of mineral supplies is represented by recycling? On the basis of the limited data published, the mineral for which recycling accounts for the highest share of total supply would appear to be lead. This reflects the dominant use of lead in the production of storage batteries. Batteries have a relatively short useful life (up to four or five years) and are readily collected and recycled.

Of the 10 other minerals cited earlier in relation to import dependency, substantial tonnages of copper, iron and steel, chromium, nickel, aluminium and tin are also recovered from old scrap.

167

Because zinc's largest use is as a coating for steel products, a lower proportion of zinc is recycled. In the case of manganese, recycling accounts for a negligible share of consumption as viable ways to recover manganese from salvaged steel or pig iron have not been found. The two non-metallic minerals — phosphates and potash — are fertilizer raw materials and neither is recyclable.

Much skill and thought has been devoted to the efficient collection, sorting and transporting of scrap. Machines devised for compacting automobiles, for example, have greatly facilitated the salvage of minerals from obsolete vehicles. Nevertheless, high costs are entailed in moving secondary materials from the dispersed geographical areas where they are generated to the locations where they are processed. Thus, prices play a major role in determining the flow of scrap to market. Astute scrap dealers are quick to sense price trends. Attempts to coerce scrap supplies into the market have invariably been unsuccessful. If market conditions are right, scrap supplies will be forthcoming in large volumes in the major industrial countries. If the market is not attractive, scrap will not be collected or, if collected, will not be sold.

Conservation in Use
Conservation implies performing a specific function with a reduced amount of raw material. Much of the technological progress of this century has consisted of improving the standard of living while conserving materials use. Examples of extensive conservation in use of minerals abound. It is appropriate to cite only a few.

Prior to World War II trans-Atlantic passenger travel was by large ocean liners. A typical 50,000-ton vessel would carry 3,000 passengers. It made a round-trip every two weeks, thus transporting 6,000 people across the broad ocean. Today trans-Atlantic travel is predominantly by jet aircraft. A single 747 jet, weighing a few hundred tons, less than 1% of the weight of a large ocean liner, will carry 350 passengers each way. Typically, it will make 12 round trips in two weeks — a total of 8,400 people. Minerals account for the bulk of the weight of both the ship and the aircraft.

Similar calculations can be made of the mineral requirements for overland travel by air compared with travel by passenger train.

A hand-held pocket calculator, weighing a few ounces, performs the same functions previously performed by desk-top office machines weighing several pounds. To conserve fuel supplies, the use of smaller passenger cars worldwide has reduced the tonnages of minerals consumed even though the number of cars produced has risen. Part of the reduction has been achieved by such developments as thinner walls for diecast zinc parts and lighter storage batteries with reduced lead content that deliver equal amounts of charge. Improved coating techniques have reduced the amount of tin required to plate a given surface of tinplate for the container industry.

These examples illustrate two quite different motives for conservation. The savings achieved in materials consumption through the development of jet aircraft and pocket calculators were the consequence of market forces resulting from technological development. The savings achieved in smaller passenger cars or improving coating techniques have been motivated by a conscious effort to reduce materials consumption. Whatever the motives, however, the effect on demand for materials has been similar — there have been dramatic savings.

When mineral supplies are limited, conservation can be achieved by rationing consumer products or by outright prohibition of manufacture of items deemed non-essential. These are extreme measures that governments are likely to invoke only in genuine emergencies. During World War II most belligerents prohibited production of passenger cars and recreation vehicles as well as a number of other items using smaller quantities of strategic materials. Germany and the United Kingdom abstained from production of many civilian goods and undertook a campaign to augment supplies by melting church bells, statues, and similar ornamental products.

Substitution

One form of conservation is to substitute a readily available commodity for one in short supply due to its import origin or other causes. Substitution is a process that has been taking place since the dawn of civilization, when the only industrial raw materials were wood, stone and copper.

The chief motive for substitution over the centuries has been economic — to find a less expensive or a more effective material to replace the traditional commodity employed in a given application. This motive is still the cause of most of the substitution that occurs currently. However, particularly in this century, added impetus for substitution has come from concerns over availability (particularly during military conflict) or over national problems such as a shortage of foreign exchange.

Public awareness of substitution was heightened during the energy crisis resulting from the rise in oil prices. The list of substitutes suggested for oil was extensive. It included coal, uranium, hydro-electric power, oil from shale and tar sands, synthetic oil from coal, alcohol from vegetable matter, steam from geothermal sources, solar energy, power generated by the tides or the wind, and wood — man's first source of energy.

Substitution can be extensive. This can be illustrated by citing what has happened in the markets for a single mineral — lead — in the years since World War II. When the war ended lead had six distinct, identifiable major markets: cable sheathing; the paint industry; lead pipe and sheet in construction; lead solders for joining metals; tetra-ethyl lead additives for gasoline; and storage batteries, chiefly for vehicular starting systems.

In the past 40 years substitutes have been developed that have replaced lead to a considerable extent (but not completely) in five of these six markets. The loss of markets has been due both to economic factors and to concern over lead's toxic properties. The latter has prompted regulations limiting lead's use.

Lead had a large share of the cable sheathing market because of its ductility and impermeability. However, its weight constituted a problem for power and telecommunications companies. They succeeded in developing as alternatives various composites of steel and/or aluminium with plastics. These weighed less than lead and had comparable properties of impermeability under most circumstances.

White lead had long been the preferred pigment for residential painting, both indoors and outdoors. Titanium dioxide has now largely replaced white lead, in part due to concern over cases of lead poisoning attributed to the use of lead-based pigments. However, lead has retained paint markets as a corrosion-inhibitor for steel structures and machinery and in safety markings on highways.

In the construction industry, lead pipe and sheet have lost ground in roofing, flashing, piping and caulking but still retain a share of the market. Plastics have replaced lead sheet in acid-resistant linings for many chemical industry applications but lead sheets continue to enjoy markets in ornamental pools and fountains.

In the field of joining metals, lead solders have been replaced by alloys of other metals in applications where high temperatures or concern over health make lead's low melting point and toxic properties inappropriate.

Until about 1970 the use of lead in gasoline additives represented a rapidly growing market. However, the perceived (though unproven) threat to public health from lead contained in vehicle emissions spreading over land adjacent to highways has since caused widespread adoption of stringent regulations limiting the lead content of gasoline. In several countries regulations have specified that cars built currently must use lead-free gasoline because automobile catalytic converters designed to deal with other polluting emissions would be rendered inoperative by lead. Although not completely eliminated, the market for additives has shrunk by more than 75%.

The one field where lead has retained its dominant position has been in the production of storage batteries. A great deal of research has been undertaken on substitutes for lead, including nickel-cadmium, lithium, zinc-air and other batteries. To date none has been developed that matches the dependability, economy, and rechargeability of the lead storage battery in the automotive and other major markets. Hence, the world's growing vehicle population provides lead with a large and stable market. Currently batteries account for more than half of all refined lead consumption.

The substitution process in lead has taken place over a prolonged period. It has entailed careful research, product design changes, and re-tooling in consumers' plants. Substitution was due to economic and health considerations rather than a desire to reduce import dependency. Despite losses, due to substitution, lead consumption in the market-economy countries set an all-time record in 1979.

When governments promote substitution in an effort to reduce import dependence, they seek quick results. Sometimes they are tempted to prohibit the use of one material and insist on substitution by another. This can cause difficulties. Delays are inevitable in making substitutions because products must be re-designed, plant facilities must be revamped to cope with a change in raw materials, and work forces must be re-trained. Substantial capital costs ensue.

Substitution dictated by materials shortages may result in unsatisfactory performance. During World War II when oil was short, the Axis belligerents and such European neutrals as Sweden and Switzerland resorted to charcoal as a fuel for automotive vehicles. Operating costs rose sharply and efficiency declined. Promptly after the War's end, vehicles were reconverted to the use of oil.

The search for substitute materials has been an ongoing process for many years. Scientific investigation continues to identify many possible avenues on which work is planned. Doubtless many significant changes lie ahead — particularly in the field of ceramics and composite materials. For the most part such changes, as in the case of lead, will be orderly and gradual, rather than abrupt overnight transitions from the use of one mineral to a substitute commodity. And, as in the case of lead, loss of a specific market to a substitute material does not necessarily cause a reduction in overall volume.

Stockpiling

Recognizing that stimulation of domestic mine production, conservation and substitution are costly and time-consuming, some strategists prefer to deal with import dependency through stockpiles of strategic and critical materials. For instance, had the United States Government held substantial stockpiles of chromite and manganese ore at the onset of World War II, the development of the uneconomic domestic resources cited earlier in this chapter would have been

172

unnecessary. Manpower, scarce equipment, large capital investments and time would have been conserved.

What are stockpiles? They are accumulations of specific materials deemed critical for defence or essential industry purposes. Ideally they are acquired in times of abundance to be held until they are needed in times of scarcity. The usual procedure is to establish individual goals for each material deemed critical or strategic. This requires assumptions as to the duration and nature of future emergencies. The aggregate cost and the availability of funds for the acquisition are prime considerations.

In essence, stockpiles are insurance against unpredictable contingencies. As with all insurance, the basic problem is to measure the cost against the perceived risks. For minerals, the initial purchase represents the major item of cost. Unlike agricultural commodities or forest products, minerals for the most part do not deteriorate while stored. The cost of bulk storage of minerals is low. Nor do minerals become obsolete, as military weapons and munitions tend to. Due to worldwide inflation, over a period of time stockpiles can be expected to enhance in value.

Monetary considerations aside, the chief attraction of stockpiles in times of emergency is that they conserve manpower, scarce equipment, and transport and energy capacity that otherwise would have to be used in the production of materials. These aspects were recognized by the U.S. Congress when, following the end of World War II, it virtually unanimously enacted legislation authorizing a massive stockpiling effort.

The Congress and the U.S. public remembered that during the war skilled miners had been granted deferment from military service even though their expertise would have been of great value to the military engineering corps. Trucks, shovels, compressors, rock drills and other tools needed by the military had to be allocated to the mining industry under high priority ratings. Energy supplies that could have expedited shipbuilding or production of explosives had to be channelled into the refining of metals. Cargo vessels, desperately needed to transport men and supplies to the fighting fronts, had been used instead to transport bulk minerals. In the judgement of many,

173

these diversions tended to prolong the war at great cost in casualties and money.

The United States' Government stockpiling programme has received great attention but other countries have either undertaken or considered stockpiles as part of their strategic planning.

Sweden and Switzerland, both neutrals during World War II, have long had ongoing programmes, details of which are not made public. Sweden grants tax concessions to private sector companies to induce them to hold strategic materials stocks in reserve. France has had a limited low-key programme. The United Kingdom had a modest stockpiling effort in the early eighties but it was largely liquidated in 1985. Japan has considered stockpiling frequently but thus far its main effort appears to have been restricted to major base metals and to be more motivated by commercial than by military considerations. Several years ago Germany F.R. debated the creation of a stockpile of those commodities which it imported from southern Africa but no formal action was taken.

In recent years the argument has been advanced that stockpiles are obsolete because the next major war is likely to be nuclear and of extremely short duration, so the logistics of materials supply will be irrelevant. Under such a scenario, conventional military forces presumably would also not play a decisive role, yet governments maintain them at great expense.

Those who believe stockpiles are desirable maintain that while nuclear war is a possibility, it is not a certainty. Therefore, they see a need for a prudent government to protect itself against the contingency of a prolonged war fought with conventional weapons.

In the United States the stockpile issue has been a subject of lively debate for many years. Strongly espoused by Presidents Truman and Eisenhower, stockpiles were attacked as excessive by President Kennedy. As a result of his raising the issue, stockpile objectives were reduced and large amounts of minerals were declared surplus and sold during his Administration and those of Presidents Johnson and Nixon.

The latter, in 1973, proposed that the amounts held in stockpile should not exceed one year's requirements because domestic produc-

tion could be increased, consumption could be reduced by conservation, and substitutes could be found for those items that the United
States did not produce.

By 1976, under President Ford, there was a return to a more
positive attitude towards stockpiles. Goals were restored to a level
deemed adequate to cover a three-year emergency. The Carter
Administration in 1980 endorsed this view, although making minor
alterations in some goals. And then in July 1985, President Reagan
proposed extensive reductions in goals to levels reminiscent of the
Nixon programme. However, Congressional opposition has thus far
blocked the Reagan proposals.

Since 1962 the goals and the value of the actual holdings of
materials in the U.S. stockpile have been a matter of public record.
When President Kennedy expressed criticism of the programme, the
stockpile at then current prices had a value of about $8,000 million,
covering more than 60 different commodities. Sales of materials
between 1962 and September 1985 netted the government somewhat
more than $8,000 million, the value of the materials held in 1963.

Between 1962 and 1979 virtually no material was bought for the
stockpile. After a revision of stockpile legislation in 1979, buying was
resumed on a modest scale and had amounted to about $400 million
by September 30, 1985. Nevertheless, the value of the materials
remaining in the stockpile on September 30, 1985, based on then
current prices, was nearly $10,000 million, largely representing
commodities acquired before 1963. This shows the substantial
appreciation in stockpile values during the life of the programme.

Those who oppose stockpiles maintain that the interest cost of
money tied up in stockpiles has been greater than the appreciation in
the value of the stockpile. While this is true, most other government
programmes represent expenditures which do not result in tangible
assets of demonstrable value and yet involve proportionate interest
costs.

Whether or not the stockpile programme has been of value to the
United States' Government, over the years it has had de-stabilizing
consequences for the minerals industry. Goals for individual minerals
have been changed frequently, sometimes being drastically increased

and at other times being reduced. For many minerals goals have at times been reduced to zero, all stocks have been liquidated, and then later new goals have been set.

Typical of the commodities affected by stockpile goal-changing has been tin. In 1973 when the Kennedy Administration first published figures, the tin stockpile amounted to 350,000 tons — equal to about two years' global consumption. This metal had been bought in the early fifties, before the International Tin Agreements came into existence. The goal has been progressively reduced since 1963 and large amounts of tin have been sold as surplus.

These sales brought repeated protests from the chief tin producing nations. At times, however, stockpile sales may actually have been of some assistance to the International Tin Council programme. The sale of 40,000 tons between July 1973 and June 1974 put some damper on the then raging tin market. During this period the market price of tin rose to double the ITC ceiling. Without stockpile sales the price would doubtless have risen much higher.

There have been other times when the stockpile has sold tin while the producing countries were under export quota restrictions and were required to support the market through additions to the buffer stock. This was the case after the 1982 recession, creating what the producers felt was an unfair addition to their burdens. To meet their objections in late 1983 the United States agreed with the Association of Southeast Asian Nations to limit stockpile sales to a rate of 3,000 tons annually for the years 1983-84. As of September 30, 1985, the stockpile goal for tin was 42,700 tons (about one year's imports of tin into the United States), the amount on hand was 185,434 tons and the balance of 142,734 tons was listed as surplus although Congress had authorized only the sale of another 20,000 tons.

The United States' experience over a period of 40 years illustrates a key weakness in relying on stockpiles to offset import dependence in times of crisis. Memories are short. The circumstances that once induced a nation to build up massive stockpiles at great cost seem less compelling to a new generation of government officials. Confronted with intractable budgetary problems, they view stockpiles as an asset that can readily be liquidated to provide needed revenues. They are prepared to cash in their insurance policies to obtain immediate funds, foregoing long-term protection.

The key elements in dealing with problems of import dependence can perhaps be summarized as follows:

1. Under peacetime conditions, import dependence rarely poses grave problems for industrialized countries. Resources of all important non-fuel minerals are ample and readily available in the market-place. Occasionally consumers in one country may face temporary shortages arising from events taking place in a supplier country. During a prolonged strike at Canadian nickel mines, British consumers were adversely affected while their foreign competitors had access to nickel from other sources. However, past efforts by supplying nations to restrict supplies in the hope of realizing excessive prices have invariably been unsuccessful in the long-run.

2. Import dependence may create serious problems in wartime or on occasions of prolonged civil disorder in countries that are key sources of certain minerals. This is particularly true of minerals production which is concentrated in only a few nations, as is the case, for instance, with chromite, platinum and cobalt.

3. Strategies available for coping with import dependence include: stimulation of domestic production; encouragement of recycling; conservation in use; substitution of more readily available commodities; and stockpiling. Each of these strategies has limitations.

4. Marginal domestic deposits require long lead times to achieve production in times of emergency, even in the case of mines that have been previously equipped and operated. Capital costs and operating costs are high. Manpower, scarce machinery and scarce supplies are required, creating diversions from a direct military effort.

5. Since recycling is an ongoing process under normal conditions, additional yields from recycling in times of emergency are likely to constitute only a modest replacement for minerals previously imported. Civilian morale may be boosted by a feeling that salvage of obsolete objects contributes to the national defence, but experience in two major wars has shown that the quantities of materials recovered are small in relation to the overwhelming emergency requirements.

6. Conservation of use is also an ongoing process. Rationing or outright prohibition of production of certain items can substantially reduce consumption of minerals for articles deemed to be non-essential, at least partially offsetting increased demand from the military and essential civilian sectors. However, if no imports are available or if imports have been drastically reduced despite conservation, a serious problem will persist.

7. Substitution under emergency conditions is likely to be costly, to result in inferior products and to take time to achieve because of designing and re-tooling requirements. Effective substitution, in terms of economics and quality of product, can be expected to be an ongoing process in peacetime.

8. Materials from stockpiles previously acquired in peacetime can be made immediately available in an emergency at an economic cost and without the manpower, transport, and equipment diversions required to develop domestic sources as a replacement for imports. However, to build adequate stockpiles requires a continuing commitment by government and the public to provide substantial sums as insurance against an unpredictable emergency at an unknown time. As the experience with the United States' stockpile has shown, with the passage of time it becomes difficult to maintain such a commitment.

This recital indicates the complexities of the problem of import dependence. Like many controversial matters, the public tends to ignore the problem until some unexpected event brings it forcibly to the forefront. This was dramatically demonstrated by the oil crisis of 1974 which made the citizens of many nations cognizant of their dependence on the supply of a single raw material that they had long taken for granted.

To expect governments to develop clear-cut policies to which they will adhere single-mindedly for extended periods is perhaps unrealistic, with the possible exception of small disciplined nations such as Sweden and Switzerland. For most industrial nations the more probable course is one of occasional periods of intense interest in access to basic mineral supplies, followed by longer intervals when attention is concentrated on other matters.

CHAPTER NINE

Minerals in the Centrally Planned Countries

Self-Sufficiency is a Major Goal

The mineral industries of the centrally-planned nations march to a very different tune than the mineral industries of the market-economy world. Under central planning the state determines prices, the level of production, the amount of consumption and the purposes for which minerals are used. Imports and exports of minerals are controlled not through tariffs or quotas but by the edict of government planners. Within the national boundaries market forces are subordinated to bureaucratic decisions.

Limited private markets for some goods are permitted to co-exist with state enterprises in some centrally-planned countries. However, these markets typically are for food and a few consumer goods. Minerals, as basic raw materials for heavy industry, remain wholly within the economic structure dictated by orthodox socialism.

What are the priorities in mineral policy for the centrally-planned countries? For the two major powers — the Soviet Union and the People's Republic of China — a major goal is to attain maximum self-sufficiency in mineral supply. Dependence on imports is viewed as a threat to national security. A second objective is financial — to conserve scarce foreign exchange. Minerals imported from countries in the market-economy sector usually must be paid for in hard currency, for which the Soviet Union and China have many other needs. If possible, imports are obtained from other centrally-planned countries that accept payment in soft currency or by barter. If not available from such friendly sources, then every effort is bent to restrict consumption so as to minimize imports.

The Soviet Union and China are vast countries with diverse geological environments. They have the potential to produce virtually every important non-fuel mineral, though some of that production may be from deposits that would be unlikely to survive competitive market forces in a free market-place.

To develop their mineral potentials the Soviet Union and China devote massive amounts of capital and manpower to long-term mining projects; resources that might otherwise be devoted to increasing the supply of consumer goods. This is the classic choice between guns and butter.

National mineral self-sufficiency is a less realistic goal for the smaller centrally-planned countries of eastern Europe — such nations as Poland, Hungary, Germany D.R. and Czechoslovakia. Within their limited domains, they lack the potential for all the mineral resources required to meet their industrial needs. Dependent on imports of many essential minerals, they first look to their COMECON partners, particularly the Soviet Union. That country in its own planning takes their requirements into account.

Thus, even though not nationally self-sufficient in mineral supply, as members of the bloc of centrally-planned countries, these allies of the Soviet Union feel reasonably secure. As for the few minerals of which these smaller countries have export surpluses, their first priority is to supply the Soviet Union to the extent it is import dependent. Any remaining quantities they eagerly sell to market-economy countries in exchange for hard currencies.

Detailed official statistics of mineral production and consumption are not published by many centrally-planned countries, including the Soviet Union and China. Analysts turn to several market-economy country organizations — including the World Bureau of Metal Statistics, the U.S. Bureau of Mines and a large metals producer in Germany F.R., Metallgesellschaft — for informed estimates. While these figures may not be exact, they provide an order-of-magnitude approximation and are available for the entire post-World War II period.

Useful clues are also provided in the import and export statistics of the principal market-economy trading nations. These reveal the extent of import dependence of centrally-planned countries for some minerals as well as the magnitude of their export surpluses of other minerals. Over the years export/import statistics also provide indications of changing trends in production capacity and consumption requirements.

Observers in the market-economy countries can feel some confidence in their conclusions about the scope of mineral production and consumption in the centrally-planned countries. Judging the economic performance of their mineral enterprises is more difficult. Cost data are not available comparable with information covering mineral enterprises in the market-economy countries. Profit-and-loss statements or balance sheets are not published for individual operations in the centrally-planned countries. Moreover, conversion of such figures, if available, into market-economy equivalents would be hampered by the absence of free market exchange rates for currencies of the centrally-planned countries.

Nevertheless, experienced mining people can draw tentative conclusions by examining data on grades of ore mined, daily production rates, stripping ratios in openpit mines, size of crews, sources of energy, distance to market and other relevant data. For example, a report of the Kazakhstan Academy of Science in 1985 commented that "nationally ore containing 0·2% copper is now considered economic". A deposit of that grade would not currently be considered economically feasible in the market-economy countries. That the Soviets are prepared to proceed with exploitation of deposits of such low grade indicates that self-sufficiency in copper supply is an important goal. Aside from military considerations, they also would prefer not to draw on hard currency reserves to import substantial quantities of minerals.

The Soviet Union — A Giant Miner

A review of the size and status of the mineral industries in several centrally-planned countries provides a perspective on their mineral policies and priorities. Clearly the first country whose mineral industry should be examined is the Soviet Union. It has had the longest experience in central planning. Its industrial establishment is the largest and its annual gross national product is now generally believed to be second only to that of the United States.

A brief statement of the Soviet mineral position following the Revolution of 1917 and before World War II is appropriate. During this period the Soviet Union was a major exporter of chromite, manganese, phosphates, asbestos, diamonds, gold and platinum. The last four minerals are not among the 11 commodities cited in previous chapters as yardsticks of production, consumption, and national self-sufficiency in the market-economy countries. Nevertheless they are significant sources of foreign exchange earnings for the Soviet Union in view of its limited credit facilities and low cash reserves.

Soviet iron ore production between the two World Wars was adequate for the modest steel industry of that period. Production of bauxite, copper, lead, nickel, tin and zinc was small by world

TABLE 12: MINE PRODUCTION OF THE SOVIET UNION
(figures in tons)

Commodity	1950	1984	Increase Between 1950 and 1983
Bauxite, gross weight	600,000(a)	4,600,000(b)	667%
Chromite, gross weight	500,000	3,300,000	560%
Copper, content	218,000	1,020,000	368%
Iron ore, gross weight	24,000,000	243,100,000	913%
Lead, content	111,600	570,000	411%
Manganese, gross weight	2,000,000	17,100,000	455%
Nickel, content	25,000	175,000	600%
Phosphate rock, concentrate	2,500,000	31,900,000	1,176%
Potash (K$_2$O equivalent)	(c)	9,500,000	
Tin, content	3,000	36,000	1,100%
Zinc, content	128,700	980,000	661%

(a) Estimated for 1948, 1950 figure not available.
(b) In addition domestic mines produced 2 million tons of nepheline and 615,000 tons of alunite used in aluminium production.
(c) Not available.

Source: *U.S. Bureau of Mines Yearbook* for 1951, *U.S. Bureau of Mines Yearbook* for 1984; World Bureau of Metal Statistics for copper, lead and nickel.

The figures for copper, lead, nickel, tin and zinc are metal contained in ores mined in the Soviet Union. Production of refined metal differed to the extent that imported raw materials or scrap were treated in Soviet metallurgical plants.

standards. This was a constraint on Soviet industrial potential since hard currency was not available to fund substantial imports.

The devastation caused by World War II left the Soviet Union faced with enormous problems. Nevertheless, the Kremlin leaders were determined to maintain a strong military establishment and to rebuild industrial facilities. They recognized that the country's population expected an improvement in living standards. To succeed on all three fronts — military, industrial, and civilian — they undertook a major expansion of mineral output. They strove to increase exports of those minerals of which the Soviet Union had long been a key producer, and to expand production of other minerals needed to broaden the industrial base.

Table 12 demonstrates the magnitude of Soviet success. It compares Soviet production of 11 key minerals in 1950 with production in 1984, as estimated by the U.S. Bureau of Mines and the World Bureau of Metal Statistics. During this period output of every commodity was increased many times, ranging from a 411% rise in lead production to a gain of 1,176% for phosphate rock. This achievement required exploration for new deposits, provision of infrastructure in extremely remote areas, massive allocations of capital and manpower and a willingness to develop resources that might not have been considered viable in a market-economy context.

A striking example of the last point is the development of the Soviet aluminium industry. To expand production the Soviet Union has exploited aluminium-bearing minerals not used by market-economy producers. For the latter, the sole raw material currently processed to recover aluminium metal is high-grade bauxite. Commercial production of bauxite in such countries as Australia, Guinea and Jamaica is from deposits with an Al_2O_3 content of over 50%. This means that four tons of bauxite will produce two tons of alumina (Al_2O_3) and two tons of alumina will produce one ton of aluminium metal.

In comparison with this ratio of four tons of raw material to produce one ton of metal, the Soviet Union's aluminium industry processes 8·5 tons of domestic raw material to recover a ton of metal, according to information published by the U.S. Bureau of Mines.

As aluminium is the most common metallic element in the earth's crust, the Soviet Union, with the largest land area of any nation, obviously has enormous aluminium resources within its boundaries. However, the deposits that have been identified thus far, while large in tonnage, are low in grade. Soviet mine production of aluminium-bearing materials in 1984 is estimated to have been 4·6 million tons of low-grade bauxite, 2·6 million tons of nepheline syenite and 615,000 tons of alunite. From this aggregate of 7·8 million tons of raw material about 900,000 tons of aluminium was produced.

To supplement this domestic raw material feed, the Soviet aluminium industry imported bauxite and alumina from abroad — chiefly Hungary, Greece and Yugoslavia. Total Soviet aluminium production in 1984 is estimated to have been 2·1 million tons, of which 55% was derived from imported raw materials. However, consumption in the Soviet Union is estimated to have been only 1·5 million tons. The balance of 600,000 tons of aluminium was exported, with Hungary being listed as a major destination. Hence, it appears that Hungarian bauxite and alumina was to a considerable extent imported for conversion and re-export rather than for internal Soviet consumption.

In terms of import reliance, the Soviet Union's position on aluminium amounts to a 40% deficiency (domestic mine supply with a content of 900,000 tons against domestic consumption of 1·5 million tons). In terms of a possible major conflict, the Soviet aluminium position is not one of great exposure, however, since three of its major import sources of raw materials are accessible by land transport. Despite Soviet political support of developing Third World nations, its trade arrangements take into account military vulnerabilities. Thus, although an extensive trade agreement covering bauxite was negotiated years ago with a left-leaning Jamaican Government, little actual trade in bauxite with Jamaica developed. In recent years the Soviet Union has imported bauxite from Guinea, but the volume is less than half of the quantity shipped by Guinea to the United States.

Among the 11 major minerals the only other one on which the Soviet Union has net import dependence is tin. Domestic tin production has risen sharply but Soviet consumption of the metal has also greatly increased, unlike the trend in the market-economy countries. Apparently there has been less substitution in areas such as solders, bronzes and brasses. Also a large share of Soviet tinplate production is by the hot-dip process, which uses more tin per unit of tinplate produced than does electrolytic coating. Most Soviet tin production is mined from Siberian lode deposits where climatic conditions are adverse and costs relatively high. Imports are obtained primarily from Malaysia and other southeast Asian sources, rather than from China.

The Soviet Union is a net importer of a number of lesser minerals — principally cobalt, fluorspar, barite and tungsten. These imports are largely derived from other centrally-planned countries — cobalt from Cuba, fluorspar and tungsten from China and Mongolia and barite from Bulgaria and Korea D.P.R. By importing from fellow socialist nations, currency problems and security risks are both minimized.

Of the nine other key minerals cited in the tabulation of import-dependence of the market-economy countries, the Soviet Union is a substantial net exporter of six — chromite, iron ore, manganese, nickel, phosphates and potash. It is essentially self-sufficient in copper, lead and zinc. For most of these materials the statistics show both imports and exports. Without undertaking an extended discussion, the following comments seem appropriate.

Chromite, iron ore and manganese are the three major bulk commodities required by the iron and steel industry. Soviet exports of these are largely, but not entirely, directed towards Poland, Germany D.R. and Czechoslovakia. These three are the most industrialized countries, other than the Soviet Union, within the COMECON bloc. By supplying them with basic raw materials the Soviet Union is able to maintain close economic ties and strengthen potential allies during a major conflict. The Soviets are not currently importers of either chromite or iron ore but recently significant quantities of high-grade manganese ore have been bought from Australia and Gabon. The average content of Soviet manganese ores has dropped to 30-31% Mn. In terms of gross weight, the Soviet

Union accounts for almost 45% of global manganese production. Despite high domestic consumption, net exports account for about 12% of Soviet manganese production.

The Soviet nickel position has been strengthened by the development of recently discovered deposits in eastern Siberia at Noril'sk. Soviet production in recent years has equalled or exceeded output in Canada, long the world's leading producer. To maintain close ties with Cuba, the first centrally-planned country in the Western Hemisphere, the Soviet Union has consistently imported large quantities of Cuban nickel, no doubt to help Cuba offset the effects of the United States embargo which has been in effect since 1962. On balance, Soviet exports of nickel are more than double its nickel imports.

The U.S.S.R. has a strong position in fertilizer raw materials. Despite phosphate production that ranks it second only to the United States, the Soviet Union has negotiated a treaty with Morocco providing for financing of a major phosphate project and substantial imports over a term of years. This arrangement provides links with a strategically placed Arab nation that commands the western entrance to the Mediterranean. Soviet phosphate exports to Bulgaria, Poland, Hungary and other of its COMECON allies exceed Moroccan imports by a wide margin. In potash, the other basic fertilizer raw material, the Soviet Union is the world's largest producer, accounting for about one-third of the total. Exports are primarily in the form of fertilizer products rather than crude potash. They are also destined largely for the COMECON nations, notably Poland and Hungary.

The Soviet Union has extensive resources of copper, lead and zinc. These have been developed to make the country basically self-sufficient. Trade statistics reveal both imports and exports of all three metals. The amounts are roughly equivalent and are small in relation to estimated domestic supplies. Imports include ores and concentrates from the market-economy countries to be processed in Soviet metallurgical plants. Sources include Sweden, Greece and the United States — an occasional supplier of copper concentrates. The largest export market appears to be Czechoslovakia which has limited base-metal potential of its own. On occasion the Soviet Union has sold copper, lead or zinc to the market-economy countries but no consistent pattern of such sales has been established.

The Soviet Union is a major producer and exporter of three high-value mineral commodities, greatly prized in the market-economy countries, for which demand in the centrally-planned countries is limited. These are gold, platinum and diamonds. The Soviet Union ranks second to South Africa in gold production, ranks with South Africa as the largest producer of the platinum group metals (platinum, palladium, iridium, rhodium, ruthenium and osmium), and ranks second to Zaire in volume of diamond output (although South Africa probably ranks first in value of diamond output, since it has a higher proportion of gem stones than Zaire or the Soviet Union).

Its COMECON allies are not significant markets for Soviet exports of gold, platinum and diamonds. These are luxury goods for which centrally-planned countries would be unprepared to pay in hard currencies. However, the market-economy countries constitute a ready market for all three commodities and it is to them that the Soviet Union directs its exports, thereby earning substantial amounts of hard currencies.

Since 1974, the volume of gold sales by centrally-planned countries has varied significantly from year to year according to the estimates of Consolidated Gold Fields, PLC, which publishes an authoritative annual review of the gold market. Chart 11, based on these estimates reveals that the volume varied inversely with the price trends. The volume of sales rose when the price declined and sales declined when the price rose. The smallest amount of gold was sold in 1980, the year of the highest average price; and the largest amount of gold was sold in 1976 when the average price was the lowest during the 12 years covered by the chart.

This pattern does not imply inept marketing. Rather it suggests that a target of export revenues has been set and that the quantity of gold offered is in relation to that target. Mine production of gold in the Soviet Union is believed to be fairly constant at about 8 million ounces annually. In addition to current output, the government holds gold reserves of an unknown amount which presumably are drawn on

CHART 11. GOLD EXPORTS BY CENTRALLY-PLANNED ECONOMIES

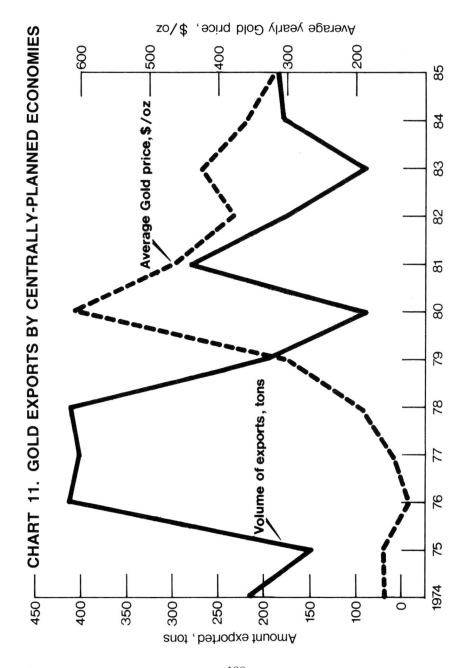

from time to time. Fabrication of gold internally is on a smaller scale in the Soviet Union than in the market-economy countries where jewellery is by far the largest source of demand.

The figures in the gold sales table are for the centrally-planned countries as a group. However, the Soviet Union is by far the largest gold producer and hence the bulk of the sales shown are doubtless for Soviet account. China has a growing gold producing industry but its output is believed to be only about one-fifth that of the Soviet Union. Korea D.P.R. also has some gold production and minor amounts are produced in Yugoslavia and Romania.

The platinum group metals are considered as precious metals because of their high price and relative rarity. Unlike gold and silver, their use for ornamental purposes or as stores of value is relatively small. The bulk of demand for these minerals is industrial, including some high-technology applications that are significant militarily. Consequently, Soviet internal demand absorbs a larger share of platinum group metal production than is the case with gold or diamonds. Current production is estimated to average about 3·6 million ounces annually (of which perhaps two-thirds is palladium and one-quarter platinum, with the balance accounted for by the four other platinum-group metals). Exports in recent years have averaged about 1·5 million ounces annually. Hard currency earnings from this trade, while significant, are much smaller than from gold.

Diamond production is divided into two qualities — gem and industrial. The boundary between these classifications is not too precise. Some material described as 'near-gem' or 'cheap-gem' quality may, on occasion, be used for industrial purposes. Soviet production divides roughly into one-third gem stones and two-thirds industrial diamonds. Most of the gem quality stones are exported to the market-economy countries because personal adornment is not encouraged in socialist societies. The greater part of the industrial diamond output, however, remains in the Soviet Union to be consumed internally.

In selling diamonds, the Soviet Union previously had a formal arrangement to market its products through the Central Selling Organization, described in Chapter 6. Although this was abrogated

189

in 1963 the view persists in the diamond market that a working relationship exists between the CSO and the Soviet diamond industry.

The Soviet Union also occupies a dominant role as a producer and exporter of asbestos. Soviet production of over 2 million tons annually accounts for approximately half of world production. Despite concern about health problems resulting from the use of asbestos in insulation and automobile brake linings, this mineral continues to play a significant role in the construction industry, particularly in asbestos-cement products. Soviet exports to COMECON countries are large but significant amounts are also sold in Western Europe in competition with imports from Canada and South Africa. About three-fifths of Soviet production is consumed at home, the balance being exported.

This review has covered only a few highlights of the Soviet mineral position. Clearly its mining industry today, in world terms, is an important factor in the market for many minerals. As on many other matters, the Kremlin is reluctant to discuss its plans and motives but there is no shortage of observers in the market-economy countries who believe they discern a master strategy that is being followed.

Among the theories advanced are: (1) that the Soviet Union is engaged in a long-term systematic strategy to deny the industrialized countries of the market-economy world access to minerals; (2) that the Soviet Union seeks privileged access to world mineral supplies for itself; (3) that the Soviet Union is plotting disturbances in countries that compete with its exports in order to secure higher prices for those exports; or (4) that for political purposes it tries to make economic mischief in league with other mineral exporters. One or more of these theories may be correct but the evidence is random and far from conclusive. The following are some conclusions that appear to be supported by the facts.

1. The Soviet Union supports leftist governments because it has always promoted international socialism. Its assistance to Cuba, Vietnam, Angola, Mozambique and Ethiopia and its invasion of Afghanistan are aspects of this policy. None of these countries is a major producer of the few minerals that the Soviet Union lacks. Nor

is any one of them a major minerals supplier to the market-economy countries. The geographical locations of these countries may present advantages to the Soviet Union in the event of a major conflict, particularly should it desire to interfere with mineral movements from other countries — but this is an incidental factor and one not likely to have provided the impelling motive for Soviet assistance.
2. The Soviet Union lacks the financial resources to engage in preclusive buying of minerals as a means of denying them to market-economy countries. Should a bidding war develop for available supplies during periods of shortage, the market-economy countries with hard currencies would certainly be winners.
3. Political disturbances in South Africa could well cause increases in prices of chromite, manganese, platinum group metals, gold, diamonds and asbestos. As the Soviet Union exports all these minerals to the market-economy countries, difficulties in South Africa could yield the Soviet Union windfall advantages. Although this may not be the chief motive for Soviet assistance to movements seeking to overthrow the South African Government, certainly the Kremlin is not unaware of the benefits it might derive from South African unrest. Meanwhile, despite the sharp ideological differences between the two countries, the evidence suggests that marketing strategies for some minerals, notably diamonds and platinum, appear to be roughly co-ordinated.
4. Soviet officials frequently assert their intention to assist developing countries by providing capital and technical expertise for new mineral projects and by expanding their imports of developing country minerals. Some new facilities have been built with Soviet assistance — metallurgical plants in India and a tin smelter in Bolivia are examples. But the Soviet Union's resources of capital and technical personnel are not sufficiently great to provide assistance for many new mineral projects in developing countries of the market-economy world. Those resources must be carefully husbanded to help expand the mineral base of other planned-economy countries. Likewise, the Soviet Union has negotiated some specific imports from developing countries, such as the instances previously cited of Moroccan phosphates and Guinean bauxite. However, the Soviet

strategy of self-sufficiency does not encourage large-scale mineral imports from Latin America, Africa or Asia. Thus, the reality falls far short of the grandiose promises.

5. The principal sources of trade and capital, as well as of technical expertise, for the developing countries continue to be the industrialized market-economy countries. Perhaps in the future some developing countries will build up large internal sources of capital, will develop cadres of trained technicians in adequate numbers and will consume large tonnages of domestically produced minerals that they now must export to sell. Until that has happened, regardless of their desire for economic independence, developing countries will rely on countries such as Britain, Japan, France, the United States and Germany F.R. for markets, capital, and technical assistance.

To sum up, in the past 40 years the Soviet Union has achieved a mammoth increase in mineral production and consumption. This has been attained at a cost. Some of its mineral output would not be viable in competitive markets. Thus, living standards have improved at a slower rate than in the market-economy countries. In many quarters, including statements made by the country's leaders, the Soviet economic position is viewed as unsatisfactory. Much of its industrial plant is believed to be inefficient or outmoded or both. The monolithic protection afforded by state control, however, enables its continued functioning.

China — Awakening to its Mineral Potential

Among the two superpowers of the centrally-planned world, the People's Republic of China ranks far behind the Soviet Union in volume of mineral production and consumption. In the early stages of the régime there was a tendency to stress the simple rural life and to prefer cottage industries to vast industrial enterprises. But more recently a strong drive has developed to create a modern industrial state that could rival the Soviet Union and the leading powers of the market-economy bloc.

How far China has to go to achieve this ambition can be illustrated by a single statistic: with roughly 25% of the world's population,

China accounts for perhaps 5% of the global consumption for most minerals. In fact, its consumption of most minerals is comparable with that of France, a country with about 4% of China's population. The 1985 estimates of consumption published by the American Bureau of Metal Statistics for the four principal base metals make this clear:

	Aluminium	*Copper*	*Lead*	*Zinc*
China	630,000	390,000	230,000	300,000
France	562,000	398,000	208,000	247,000

Figures in metric tons.

For all four of these minerals, China is still partially import dependent. The volume of imports varies sharply from year to year, depending on the availability of foreign currency reserves, the level of domestic production and the state of the consuming industries.

Although China is an ancient civilization with remarkable cultural achievements, its orientation until recently was agricultural rather than industrial. As a consequence, the extent of its mineral resources was largely unknown except for a few commodities — tin, tungsten and antimony — of which it has long been ranked as a leading producer. Since the establishment of the People's Republic in 1949, efforts have been made to explore and map the country's minerals. Clearly they are extensive but the full potential is far from being determined. Moreover, the heavy capital cost of bringing newly discovered mineral assets into production creates severe problems for China's leaders.

Chinese policy is, if at all possible, to avoid incurring substantial external debt. The Chinese have limited internal capital. Their exports are small and generate only limited amounts of hard currency. How is the country to pull itself up by its own bootstraps in the effort to become a modern industrial state?

One mineral industry that appears to offer some promise is gold mining. The Chinese are well aware that the Soviet Union generates substantial amounts of hard currency by exporting the product of its large gold mining industry. They also are fully cognizant of the substantial rise in gold prices since 1971. So the Chinese have sought, with considerable success, to stimulate gold output.

193

A substantial share of that output appears to come from the exploitation of placer deposits that require little capital but vast amounts of manpower — a resource that China possesses in abundance. Underground gold mining is also less capital-intensive than mining of bulk minerals. Statistics on China's gold production are imprecise, but estimates place the volume at close to 2 million ounces a year and growing rapidly.

To expand production of bulk minerals, the initial effort after 1949 was concentrated on scores or even hundreds of small-scale enterprises. This proved inefficient and unproductive. In the late '70s and early '80s a change in policy was enunciated. Foreign private sector corporations were invited to participate in joint-venture arrangements with the Chinese Government covering numerous large-scale undertakings in steel, aluminium, copper and other projects. Many of these were expected to require investments in the billions of dollars. Japanese, Germany F.R., United States and other leading foreign corporations were designated as potential joint venturers. Most of these plans have not yet materialized, presumably due to inability to reach detailed understandings on issues of taxation, currency conversion rights, rates of recapture of investment and similar matters.

Meanwhile, as Chinese mineral requirements gradually rise, the country is largely self-sufficient for several minerals and import-dependent for others. Of the 11 basic minerals that have been previously analyzed in relation to the market-economy countries and the Soviet Union, tin is the only commodity of which China is a consistent net exporter. And even for tin its exports have tended to decline as local demands have expanded.

Chinese production of iron ore, manganese, and nickel appears to be adequate to support the country's steel industry, which is estimated to produce about 40 million tons of crude steel annually. The chromite position is unclear. Data are unavailable on domestic production; imports are modest, primarily from the Philippines which is a source of ores chiefly suitable for making refractories but not widely used elsewhere for metallurgical purposes. Possibly Chinese requirements for metallurgical purposes are as yet small.

Bauxite production is evidently ample to meet the domestic aluminium reduction plants' requirements, with an occasional small surplus available for export to Japan. However, China is a net importer of aluminium metal as its domestic reduction capacity is insufficient for the present level of consumption.

China imports copper in ores, concentrates, blister and refined metal. Large low-grade copper deposits have been discovered that will require enormous investments if they are to become producers. Until capital has been found and plants built, China is unlikely to be self-sufficient in copper. Similar conclusions are warranted for lead and zinc, despite the existence of some domestic production. Chinese purchases of these metals are undertaken when hard currency reserves become available, so the pattern of buying is erratic.

China is a large producer of phosphates but a small producer of potash. It is a net importer of both these minerals, to a considerable extent in the form of fertilizer products rather than as minerals.

This brief summary indicates that China lags far behind the Soviet Union in its degree of current mineral self-sufficiency. This is primarily due to lack of existing capacity rather than an absence of basic resources. To create the needed capacity will require time and sacrifices — the postponement of increased supplies of consumer goods while new mineral projects are being financed. Lifting itself up by its own bootstraps to become a modern industrial state promises to be a difficult task for the Chinese Government. The determination to proceed appears to be great.

Minerals in the Other Centrally-Planned Countries

The smaller centrally-planned countries have mineral industries of varying size and diversity. They also differ in the degree of industrialization, the extent to which they are firmly within the economic and political orbit of the Soviet Union or China and their willingness to trade with the West. The following is a brief account.

Albania — This small fiercely independent country is a world-class producer of chromite and ferro-chromium. It mines copper, iron ore and nickel in sufficient quantities to be self-sufficient. For the other minerals it is import dependent but due to its small population and limited industrial development, this is not a major drain on its financial resources.

Bulgaria — Traditionally a client state of the Soviet Union, Bulgaria mines copper, iron ore, lead, manganese and zinc. It has export surpluses of the base metals but supplements its domestic production of iron ore and manganese with imports from the Soviet Union, which is also its chief source of phosphates and potash. Lacking an aluminium reduction industry, it is not an importer of bauxite and its tin and nickel requirements, which are met with imports, are minimal.

Cuba — The only important mineral product is nickel, with associated cobalt. There is a modest output of copper, exported as concentrate. Formerly a producer of iron ore and manganese, Cuba has no recorded current yield of either. Chromite is a constituent of some of its nickel ores but is not being recovered. Nickel exports are directed to the Soviet Union and Western Europe. U.S. embargo regulations have been a deterrent factor in some directions, since finished products with a demonstrable content of Cuban nickel have been turned back at U.S. ports. Cuban imports of minerals as such, other than fertilizers, are limited but the mineral content of finished goods supplied by the Soviet Union and some industrialized market-economy countries is significant.

Czechoslovakia — For its size, this country has a large industrial establishment which requires appreciable quantities of mineral raw materials. As its domestic non-fuel minerals industry is small the country's degree of import dependence is comparable with such market-economy industrial nations as Japan and Italy. Trade is largely (but not entirely) orientated towards other centrally-planned countries, notably the Soviet Union with which its political ties are close. One exception is tin, for which its chief sources are Indonesia and the United Kingdom.

Germany D.R. — The German Democratic Republic, much like Germany F.R., is heavily industrialized and has only limited production of non-fuel minerals. Although official trade statistics are not made public, its import dependence is great. Potash is the only major mineral in which it appears to be self-sufficient. Limited mine production of copper, nickel, tin and iron ore supplies only a small fraction of the country's requirements (a bare 1% in the case of iron ore). For the other major commodities it must look entirely to foreign sources, chiefly the Soviet Union and other COMECON countries but there is a significant volume of trade with Germany F.R.

Hungary — Less highly industrialized than Czechoslovakia or Germany D.R. but, nevertheless, a significant mineral consumer, Hungary's major non-fuel mineral product is bauxite, much of which it converts to alumina. It has a small production of iron ore and manganese, but imports large amounts, including ferromanganese, for its steel industry. For the other minerals it is heavily dependent on the Soviet Union, Poland and Yugoslavia, although there is some trade with market-economy countries. Exports of bauxite and alumina are shipped to Czechoslovakia, Poland and Austria as well as the Soviet Union.

Korea D.P.R. — Korea D.P.R. is a substantial producer and net exporter of lead, zinc and gold, is close to self-sufficiency in copper and iron ore and has a modest output of phosphates. It is entirely import dependent for bauxite, chromite, manganese, nickel, potash and tin. Its consumption of minerals is much smaller than the Republic of Korea's, where industrial production is several times greater.

Poland — The most populous of the COMECON countries other than the Soviet Union, Poland is a substantial producer of copper, lead and zinc. It is heavily import dependent for iron ore and has no current mine production of bauxite, chromite, manganese, phosphates, potash or tin. A small nickel mining venture was terminated in 1983 due to extremely low grade of ore and high costs. The Polish

197

copper industry has been developed in the past 20 years with capital and technology from the market-economy countries. Substantial amounts of copper are exported to Western Europe.

Romania — Although Romania produces bauxite, copper, iron ore, lead, manganese and zinc, trade statistics show supplemental imports of each of these minerals. It is wholly import dependent for chromite, nickel, phosphates, potash and tin. Romania has made efforts to develop trade with the market-economy countries, particularly the developing nations of Latin America and Africa, yet the bulk of its mineral commerce is with other centrally-planned nations.

Yugoslavia — Yugoslavia has consistently endeavoured to maintain an independent posture in political and economic matters, in line with the policies laid down by its former leader, Marshal Tito, shortly after the end of World War II. Complete statistics of Yugoslav mineral production are published. It is a large miner of bauxite, copper, lead and zinc and is self-sufficient in iron ore. Its manganese and nickel is inadequate for its own needs. Efforts are being made to develop domestic phosphate deposits. For chromite, potash and tin it is import dependent. Trade in minerals is divided equally between the centrally-planned and the market-economy nations.

Lacking the geographical extent or the geological diversity of the two centrally-planned giants — the Soviet Union and the People's Republic of China — the smaller nations that practise socialist doctrines fall far short of individual mineral self-sufficiency. As a group, however, they are well endowed with bauxite, chromite, copper, lead, nickel and zinc. They look to the Soviet Union for most of their import needs for iron ore, manganese, phosphates and potash. China supplies at least a portion of their tin needs.

Trade With the Market-Economy World
What is the aggregate share of the world's mineral production, consumption and trade represented by the centrally-planned coun-

tries? Absence of official statistics makes precise calculation difficult but one can arrive at approximations based on published estimates. The figures for world mineral production published by the U.S. Bureau of Mines suggest that the centrally-planned countries as a group account for between 20%-30% of total world output of most minerals. Comparable estimates are not available on consumption in the centrally-planned countries. Given the evidence of available trade statistics, consumption shares for the bulk commodities appear to be about equal to production shares.

The picture is perhaps clearest for the major non-ferrous refined metals. The World Bureau of Metal Statistics regularly compiles data on trade in aluminium, copper, lead, nickel and zinc between the centrally-planned and the market-economy nations. These figures reveal that in 1984, the centrally-planned countries (the East) had net exports of 188,200 tons of aluminium and 37,100 tons of nickel; and had net imports from the market-economy countries (the West) of 18,300 tons of copper, 57,800 tons of lead, and 271,000 tons of zinc. These balances of trade are modest indeed in relation to estimated world production in 1984 of 15·9 million tons of aluminium, 745,500 tons of nickel, 9·5 million tons of copper, 5·3 million tons of lead, and 6·6 million tons of zinc.

Comparable data are not published for the other six bulk minerals but Soviet and Albanian exports of chromite and Soviet exports of manganese to the West are substantial. Neither of these commodities is shipped in significant amounts from market-economy countries to centrally-planned countries. For iron ore, phosphates and potash, with the possible exception of China, the centrally-planned bloc enjoys basic self-sufficiency. However, as a group, they are substantially import dependent on the West for tin. China exports tin but the amount is much less than the deficiency in tin supply of the other centrally-planned countries.

If trade in the 11 bulk minerals between the market-economy and centrally-planned countries is relatively modest in volume, much larger values are involved in the export of gold, platinum metals and diamonds by the Soviet Union to the Western countries. Indeed, apart from exports of energy materials, gold is undoubtedly the chief

199

source of hard currency earnings for the Soviet Union. As indicated, China is now also hoping to improve its trading posture through expansion of gold production and exports.

For the present, China's options are few. It hopes to duplicate the Soviet position of basic self-sufficiency but that goal is still a long way away in terms of a modern industrial economy.

Meanwhile, because of strained relations and meagre transport potential to and from the Soviet Union, a relatively high proportion of Chinese mineral trade is with market-economy countries. Internal struggles continue within the Chinese hierarchy between those who wish to liberalize the industrial structure and those who cling to the austere traditions of the Mao régime. If the former prevail, foreign participation through capital and technical assistance may permit a considerable expansion of Chinese mineral production. If, however, the country turns its back on outside help, the rate of growth in Chinese mineral output is likely to be very gradual — as it was for the first 20 years after the People's Republic was established.

As for the Eastern European countries in the COMECON bloc pact, despite their desires to earn hard currencies through mineral exports to the market-economy nations, with a few exceptions they seem likely to continue to be closely tied to the Soviet industrial machine. Most of their mineral exports will flow eastward towards the U.S.S.R. and for those commodities which they do not produce, the Soviet Union will remain a principal source.

The world's mineral trade is not divided into two watertight compartments. There is trade between the centrally-planned countries and the market-economy countries. However, the extent of trade between the two segments is modest in comparison with the volume of trade within each segment. From time to time announcements are made of the intention to break down the barriers — to greatly expand East/West commerce. However sincere these intentions may be, the difficulties of blending two widely differing approaches to trade are great. In the centrally-planned countries control is tight; trade is rigidly directed by central bureaucracies. In the market-economy countries for the most part trade is unstructured — hectic, competitive and largely free from state intervention.

CHAPTER TEN

Looking Ahead

What lies ahead for the non-fuels minerals industry? As constituted today it bears little resemblance to the industry projected in the studies published 35 years ago by the prestigious Paley Commission.

Then the Commission anticipated that dwindling supplies of minerals would be overtaken by a tidal wave of consumption. Concerned that global economic growth would be limited, if not entirely prevented, by mineral scarcities, the Commission characterized the problem as "one of running faster and faster in order even to stand still".

This view was shared in other later studies of minerals availability. The 1972 report of the Club of Rome anticipated that resource shortages would impose severe "limits to growth" by the turn of the century.

Had these expectations been correct, by now serious recurring shortages should have developed. This is particularly the case since actual consumption of mineral resources — both fuels and non-fuels — has reached levels far beyond the Paley forecasts. Although the growth rate of mineral consumption has diminished since 1973, due to a combination of macro-economic and technological developments, current consumption of most minerals exceeds the Paley estimates by large percentages. And still the persistent scarcity forecast in the Paley study has yet to appear. Capacity to produce minerals exceeds the level of demand.

What happened to convert scarcity to abundance? Why did shortages fail to develop? The answer is successful mineral exploration. The very fact that shortages had been predicted triggered a massive increase in the post-war search for new mineral deposits. The old maxim — "Seek and ye shall find" — proved astonishingly accurate.

In the decades of the thirties and forties (apart perhaps from a brief spurt in exploration for gold deposits) the seeking had been restricted and consequently the finding had been limited as well. During those years the combination of a severe economic depression followed by the world's most devastating military conflict had diverted manpower and money from the search for minerals.

Chapter 2 has provided some details of the high discovery rates that ensued from the renewal of vigorous exploration in the post-war years. The success achieved exceeded the expectations of even the optimists among the experts. It convincingly refuted the fears of the pessimists. Not only were more prospectors looking in more places for new mineral deposits but the techniques they employed were more effective and more sophisticated. Theories of ore genesis have evolved that have led to significant finds of deposits that are not exposed on surface. The science of geophysics coupled with the use of aircraft has enabled the search to be extended to previously inaccessible regions.

Looking ahead, Harold O. Seigel in *Mining Annual Review 1985* (marking the 150th anniversary of *Mining Journal*) predicts further major advances in exploration geosciences, stressing particularly the prospect for wider use of geochemistry to obtain a better under-standing of dispersion patterns of the elements in the surface environment and in the bedrock. Orbiting satellites are expected to allow better positioning for airborne geophysical surveys. He antici-pates the development of less costly methods of drilling. This will reduce the high risk venture capital required for mineral exploration projects.

As of today, instead of the dwindling reserves of poor quality ores that had been forecast, reserves of most minerals are several times greater than the estimates made at mid-century. While many new deposits are low-grade, in other cases the quality of the new discoveries is as good as or better than the quality of the deposits mined 40 and 50 years ago.

Public imagination in recent years has been captivated by the potential for obtaining minerals from the deep ocean floor, from the frozen continent of Antarctica and even perhaps from the moon. Man's success in space exploration and in the frontiers of scientific development combine to convince the lay public that anything is possible. And, indeed, the technology exists that would make deep ocean mining and mining in Antarctica feasible. Vast resources doubtless exist in both these areas.

But technical feasibility and economic viability are not necessarily synonymous. At prevailing levels of mineral costs and prices, the prospect for early exploitation of deep sea or Antarctic deposits appears dim for the balance of this century — and perhaps far beyond. As for the moon, until the costs of space travel and life support on the moon's surface are drastically reduced, commercial mining of lunar deposits appears entirely impractical — even if these were easily located orebodies of solid gold or platinum — let alone green cheese.

Because the rate of discovery has exceeded the rate at which consumption is currently expanding, a growing backlog of identified deposits of many minerals has been established and is awaiting exploitation. This situation has rarely existed in the past. During the era of post-war expansion, mining companies were able to finance and bring into production those discoveries that appeared viable under prevailing market conditions at a rate that kept pace with growing demand.

Thus the decades of the fifties through the seventies saw the emergence of major new world producers of such minerals as copper, bauxite, lead and zinc which became formidable competitors of the previously dominant firms.

Even after the energy crisis of 1974 the momentum of expansion continued and a number of major projects were launched despite faltering markets. Gradually, however, perceptions of prospects for future market growth changed. Massive properties that had been proved by intensive exploration, with grades comparable with existing producers, were unable to obtain the capital necessary to undertake production. In due course they will doubtless be developed. Meanwhile, they constitute assurance that the kind of protracted scarcity feared by the Paley Commission and similar studies will not develop for many years to come.

The Investment Climate for Minerals

Many factors have contributed to the restricted number of new mineral projects initiated in recent years. These include:

Uncertainties in the political sphere

The erratic course of prices at a time of inflationary cost increases

The financial problems facing corporations and governments involved in mineral undertakings

The high interest rates that add a severe capital cost component in the calculation of cash flows

The widespread impression among investors that their most attractive opportunities lie in high technology and service industries rather than in capital intensive businesses such as mining.

Each of these elements has played a role in the slow-down of capital expenditure on new mining projects.

But without doubt the overriding factor weighing heavily on prospective investors is their perception of prospects for future world consumption of the mineral involved — be it aluminium, copper, phosphates or whatever. This is readily demonstrated by observing the readiness with which capital continues to flow into new gold mining ventures.

Although the price of gold has fluctuated widely since 1971, worldwide search for new gold deposits has flourished. Major mineral corporations not previously engaged in gold mining have undertaken gold exploration as a major corporate strategy. Their efforts have been rewarded by major discoveries which have whetted their appetites for still more intensive prospecting for gold.

Why is this? Managements of these companies believe that gold will continue to command a ready market as a store of value. Even though gold may not be required for industrial or monetary purposes, the public appears prepared to absorb available offerings. Despite fluctuations, the price has remained at levels well above the average cost of production from new discoveries. Corporate managers apparently see little risk that the market for gold will collapse or that they will be unable to dispose of their output.

Producers of other minerals feel less confident about the existence of a market for their products at remunerative prices. From time to time the market for base metals or non-metallics may witness temporary spurts of buying interest when demand includes quantities not needed for immediate consumption. Industrial users who fear shortages may buy to increase their inventories as a hedge against future requirements. Security considerations may induce governments to buy minerals for national stockpiles. Or speculators, anticipating price increases, may make purchases in the hopes of realizing capital gains.

However, such buying has proved an evanescent source of demand. It can disappear as quickly as it arises. For the base metals and non-metallics there is no continuing market corresponding to the willingness to accumulate precious metals — particularly gold — that is based on a belief that they constitute hedges against political uncertainty or currency inflation.

Prospects for Consumption

Thus, for investors considering long-term commitments to major new mineral projects, other than precious metal mines, the prospects for actual consumption of the specific mineral over an extended period of time must be a major preoccupation. How can those prospects best be evaluated?

Re-stating briefly some of the factors influencing mineral consumption trends already described in Chapter 1, the period since 1950 can be divided into two major segments. During the early years (1950-74) expansion of mineral consumption was vigorous, interrupted occasionally by brief downturns in the business cycle. During the latter years (since 1975) growth rates have been perceptibly lower and the recessionary setbacks have been more pronounced.

Consumption patterns in the market-economy world are best analyzed by segregating the data for three markets: (1) the United

States; (2) the other industrialized countries; and (3) the developing world. The United States had emerged from World War II with an expanded industrial structure intact and with a population that already enjoyed high standards of living. Starting from this already high base of mineral consumption, the United States market grew at a slower pace than elsewhere during the post-war period. In general, U.S. consumption corresponded to forecasts made by the Paley Commission.

The industrialized countries of Western Europe and Japan experienced a high rate of growth of mineral consumption. They had to rebuild their war-shattered industrial plant and their infrastructure of transport and utilities. Subsequently they achieved great success in advancing the living standards of their people to levels far above those that existed pre-war.

The developing countries of Asia, Latin America and Africa had not been substantial consumers of minerals pre-war. Starting from this insignificant base, they did show sharp increases by 1974 but this was primarily the consequence of an explosive rate of population increase. Their *per capita* consumption of minerals remained small, averaging perhaps one-tenth of that prevalent in the industrialized nations.

In the changed economic atmosphere following the energy crisis induced by advancing oil prices since 1974, most previous estimates of future mineral consumption trends have been sharply reduced. Previous forecasts had largely been based on extrapolation of prevalent trends, such as sustained growth in aluminium consumption at a compound annual rate of 8% or corresponding figures of 6% for nickel and 4% for copper. Many analysts, wishing to indicate that their assumptions were conservative, tended to make new forecasts at somewhat lower rates — but simple straight-line projections of demand continued to be a favourite tool during much of the seventies. More recently, somewhat more sophisticated approaches have been adopted. Thus, attention is now centred on a study of what economists call 'intensity of use'.

This approach identifies consumption of raw materials with the several stages of industrial development. Intensity of use is low in undeveloped nations that rely primarily on agricultural or pastoral production. Intensity of use increases rapidly as countries become industrialized, particularly in the phase of developing infrastructure of transport, power, telecommunications and new plant facilities. Once this basic infrastructure is in place, the theory of intensity of use is that *per capita* consumption of minerals may actually decline as an economy becomes increasingly tied to high technology and service industries that require a lower input of raw materials in relation to the value of their products and services.

During the period of 1950-74 the developing countries were largely in the first stage; Western Europe and Japan were in the second stage; and the United States was in the third stage.

By 1974 Western Europe and Japan had succeeded in restoring an effective industrial infrastructure. In many respects, with modern plants, they had become more efficient producers of many types of goods than their United States competitors. In the field of durable consumer goods, their populations were now provided with amenities such as cars, refrigerators and washing machines on a scale comparable with that enjoyed by United States citizens. These countries were poised to move out of the second stage of industrial development and to join the United States in the third stage. Hence, their mineral consumption could not be expected to continue increasing at the rapid pace that prevailed in the years 1950-74.

Thus, many observers judged that prospects for future vigorous expansion in mineral consumption would rest largely on the extent to which developing nations emerged from the first stage of industrial development and moved into the second stage. In particular, attention centred on the more populous developing nations — including notably India, Brazil, Mexico, Indonesia and the Republic of Korea.

In 1974 hopes for industrialization of these countries ran high. But in the years that followed, the distortions in world trade that ensued from the energy crisis caused sober re-appraisals. Rising interest rates placed heavy burdens on countries that had incurred substantial foreign debts because they lacked internal capital resources adequate to finance development. Upheavals in exchange rates complicated all international financial transactions. As two severe recessions created extensive surplus plant capacity in the industrialized countries, incentives to create still more capacity in the developing countries greatly diminished.

So, if it is correct that expansion of mineral consumption largely depends on industrial development by countries in stage two, the sober reality of the decade of the eighties is that few nations are now in that phase of their development.

Loss of Markets to New Materials

Concepts of future mineral consumption trends have also been recently and significantly affected by a secular factor — rapid technological developments in composite materials and ceramics. These are being evaluated as substitutes for metals in many of their traditional markets. To the extent that they succeed, they will require large amounts of some non-metallic minerals. Moreover, to a considerable extent composites are derived from petroleum-based feedstocks and so in the long-term will be affected by the availability of oil resources.

Substitution of these new materials is not, as had earlier been predicted, due to soaring mineral prices resulting from exhaustion of low-cost reserves. Mineral prices have not risen disproportionately to the prices of other goods — indeed, in many cases they have lagged behind inflationary rates.

Instead, the switch from metals to composites or ceramics is largely occurring as a consequence of performance characteristics. Thus fibre optics are replacing copper in telecommunications because with fibre optics a single cable of dimensions similar to a copper cable can carry many more messages. In the automotive industry applications for composite materials and ceramics are being considered in order to achieve weight savings or improve manufacturing techniques or obtain greater fatigue or corrosion resistance.

Clearly, modern technology provides many options, competition between materials is vigorous and manufacturers will continually evaluate the merits of rival materials before deciding which commodity combines the best performance characteristics with the greatest economy. The existence of this competition should dispel concerns previously held that monopoly or cartel control of a raw material can be used to unfairly exploit the public interest for private profit.

How will minerals fare under this rugged competitive atmosphere? Is their role in the world's economy facing a period of stagnation or even actual decline? Some believe that markets for metals will shrink even in periods of general economic growth. The difficulties of forecasting long-term consumption patterns have been illustrated by the Paley Report experience. Just as that report greatly under-estimated mineral consumption in the third quarter of this century, so perhaps the pendulum may swing abruptly in the other direction. An actual reduction in consumption may lie ahead.

To this observer, however, it seems highly unlikely that the forward momentum of mineral consumption is about to come to a full stop. Undoubtedly there will be substantial erosion of some mineral markets — two examples have been cited in the telecommunications and automotive fields. Yet the diversity of minerals use is so great and the pressure of population growth is so persistent that the probabilities favour continued, though slower, increases in the quantities of non-fuel minerals required by world industry. If a formula can be found by which living standards in the developing countries are substantially improved, then the present pessimistic appraisal of future minerals demand by some economists would indeed be confounded.

Why Mineral Prices have Held the Line
With few exceptions, prices of non-fuel minerals over the years since World War II have, like other basic commodities, barely kept pace with the rate of inflation. Year-to-year fluctuations in the prices of some commodities have been violent but the longer-term trend has been similar to the trends observed in agricultural, forest-product and livestock prices. Certainly the rise in mineral prices has been far less pronounced than the rise in prices of many manufactured goods and services.

In the United States, which has experienced less inflation than most countries, the prices in current dollars of automobiles, men's shirts, daily newspapers or urban public transport in 1985 were 10 or more times the cost of those items in 1946. The prices of most non-fuel minerals in 1985 ranged between four and six times the prices that prevailed in 1946. Tables 8 and 9 (pages 146 and 148), based on prices in the United States, demonstrate that earlier fears of sharply escalating mineral prices were groundless.

What accounts for this and what are the implications for the longer-term future?

Just as advances in exploration technology resulted in massive discoveries that disproved the theory of limited mineral resources, so improvements in the techniques of extracting and processing minerals have alleviated the cost of providing industry with its required mineral raw materials. Confronted with the problem of handling huge tonnages of low-grade materials, the mining industry and its equipment suppliers have combined to develop machines and mining methods that permit significant economies of scale. Productivity of the individual worker has risen dramatically, enabling employers to extract equal tonnages with smaller crews or larger tonnages with unchanged crews.

Research to develop still greater efficiency and productivity is an ongoing process. In his contribution to *Mining Annual Review* 1985, Sir Arvi Parbo made some startling and prescient observations. He ventured the opinion that by 2135 — 150 years forward — there will hardly be any miners underground. Minerals will be won either by robotized machinery or by *in situ* extraction of the valuable ingredients. He suggested that biotechnology will be increasingly employed *in situ* to convert metals into a readily soluble form. Mineral processing would then become largely a matter of handling solutions, thus obviating the need for crushing and grinding.

This is indeed a long look forward. One must recognize that such radical changes rarely occur overnight. The conversion to new technology is more likely to be gradual than abrupt. Present processes and present investments will not suddenly become obsolete. Existing mines and plants will continue to use traditional procedures while new projects embodying the new techniques are tested and perfected.

But, considering how profoundly the industry has changed within the lifetime of those now engaged in it, further dramatic changes doubtless do lie ahead. The cumulative effect of change will be to keep mineral prices competitive in the industrial market-place.

The mining industry, already highly capital intensive, will become even more so. New processes, more mechanization, greater dependence on automation and on computerized controls will steadily increase the up-front investment in mineral projects. This, in turn, will mean that a higher proportion of total costs will represent interest on and amortization of original investment and, at the same time, there will be a decline in the share of costs represented by labour and supplies once operations have begun.

Thus, the initial investment decision — whether or not to proceed with a new mineral project — will become ever more critical. As more money must be committed prior to start-up, judgements as to costs, quality of ore, market conditions, interest rates and the future value of cash flows will become more difficult. Faced with these uncertainties, entrepreneurs undertaking new projects will be increasingly tempted to deplete known ore reserves at a faster rate over relatively short periods of time.

Incentives for Accelerating Rates of Deposit Depletion

When interest rates were 5%, the typical new mining project was projected to mine identified ore reserves over a 20-year life. Calculations on this basis indicated a satisfactory return on investment and an appropriate life span for buildings and major items of equipment. With interest rates at 10% or more, however, operators plan faster rates of depletion of known reserves, thus realizing substantial cash flows early, enabling quick debt retirement and minimizing aggregate interest costs.

However valid such considerations may be for the individual project, in the aggregate they act to create excess productive capacity. Moreover, once a project is launched, the underlying assumptions of maximizing early cash flow mandate full-scale plant operation regardless of market conditions. Combined with the existing strategy of public sector corporations to maintain high operating rates in order to maximize employment and foreign exchange earnings, the consequence has been the creation of unwieldy surpluses overhanging markets in times of recession.

Efforts to isolate such surpluses in ways that would minimize their adverse impact on prices have been made from time to time — the most notable example being the efforts by governments of producing and consuming countries to stabilize tin prices through the International Tin Agreement, cited in Chapter 6. Frequently hailed as a model for international commodity agreements, after almost 30 years of operations the system collapsed in late 1985. Heavy financial losses were incurred. Operations on the London Metal Exchange were seriously affected.

Nevertheless, despite this failure, doubtless other efforts to control or moderate the movement of prices of mineral commodities will be attempted in the future. That any scheme can be devised which would be sufficiently flexible to cope with the complexities of a global market economy over the long term seems highly doubtful.

For most minerals the market-place can be likened to a dance in which the four performers are supply, demand, cost and prices. The tunes to which they dance are determined by the macro-factors of the global economic environment. The tunes are constantly changing. At times the melodies are gay and lilting, reflecting a cheerful environment of business upturn. At other times, the melodies are sombre and slow as the economy experiences recession.

Of the four dancers, two — demand and prices — respond quickly to the economy's music, hastening their pace when the tune is gay and dragging their feet when the tune is sombre. Unfortunately, in the minerals business the two other dancers — production and costs — seem less attuned to the music they hear. For reasons elaborated earlier, they have difficulties in adjusting quickly to changed economic circumstances. Mines are loath to curtail or close when demand dwindles and there are inevitable time lags in increasing output when demand revives.

Sticking to this figure of speech, even though the dancing partners at times seem ill-matched, they are nevertheless inevitably linked to each other — supply with demand, costs with prices. Under the circumstances, to avoid tripping over his partner's feet too frequently, each dancer will do well to watch that partner closely.

Perhaps somehow, sometime, somewhere, a magical formula will be devised that will avoid excessive volatility in mineral prices while retaining a degree of responsiveness to radically changing circumstances. That would mark the millenium for the mineral industries.

Absent such a development, the presumption must be that mineral prices will continue to fluctuate. The fluctuations will be greatest in those metals that bear the full brunt of cyclical swings in the economic cycle. They will be more moderate for those commodities, such as many of the non-metallics, that are less susceptible to cyclical trends in the economy.

Given this outlook, managements of mineral enterprises must be prepared to face hard decisions at times of marked imbalance between supply and demand or when costs are out of phase with prices. Managements of established private sector companies that have long had their primary focus on mining have grown accustomed to, although they are not happy with, the need for making such decisions.

To those whose experience with the industry has been relatively brief, the complexities and seeming incongruities of the minerals industry must come as a considerable shock. This includes both political officers of governments that have formed public sector companies to operate domestic mines and executives of some of the diversified private sector enterprises that have absorbed non-fuel minerals operations in recent years.

The Need for Flexible Approaches

The choices are seldom clear-cut. Any course of action proposed is likely to result in drawbacks as well as advantages. A typical example is provided by the history of the Ok Tedi project in Papua New Guinea. A former official of the government of that country, William

S. Pintz, has ably described in his book *Ok Tedi — Evolution of a Third World Mining Project* (published by Mining Journal Books Ltd, 1984) the conflicting priorities faced by the government team negotiating a long-term arrangement with the consortium formed to exploit the mine.

The Papua New Guinea Government views the project from three perspectives. It is a stockholder, having exercised its option to acquire a 20% interest in the project, and as a stockholder it has an interest in profits. It is a tax collector, relying on several categories of taxes to raise revenues to meet governmental budgets. And it is a regulator, concerned that a major mining operation in a remote part of the country should not unduly disturb the indigenous population and the somewhat fragile environment. Obviously within the government itself the priorities of individual officials are heavily influenced by their individual responsibilities.

In due course a satisfactory agreement was reached which provided the managers of the project and their bankers with what they then considered adequate safeguards to protect their investment. In the negotiations, according to Pintz, there had been an absence of the kind of political rhetoric that had prevailed at some other previous negotiations between host governments of the Third World and foreign investors.

After the agreement went into effect, unforeseen contingencies developed. A drought added heavily to the cost of moving equipment and supplies by making an access river unnavigable, a dam collapsed and there were protracted periods of low copper prices, to mention only a few.

To cope, new arrangements were needed. The venture has proved to be a learning experience not only for the P.N.G. Government but also for the management representing the private investors. Despite some periods of confrontation, the parties have been able to reconcile their differences to date. As of mid-1986, the project has become a major gold producer and is about to initiate the first stage of its copper production plans.

The Ok Tedi experience is recited at some length because it illustrates the underlying need for flexible approaches to the solution of mining problems. All contingencies cannot be foreseen in the early stages of a mining project. Unexpected events, not anticipated by any of the parties involved, can so change the parameters of the undertaking as to require revision of an original arrangement.

George Santayana, the American philosopher, once observed that those who do not learn from the mistakes of the past are doomed to repeat them. In an industry so vast and so complex as the minerals industry, one cannot expect the participants to be aware of all past events — or much less to be able to foresee the twists and turns the future may bring.

The minerals industry experienced a major transformation in the post-war years. The transfer of much mineral property ownership from foreign private investors' hands to the control of host governments in the developing countries was in some cases an orderly procedure carried on with relative goodwill on both sides. In other cases it occasioned unpleasant confrontations and bitter accusations of unfairness or outright dishonesty by both parties. Time is said to heal all wounds and doubtless much of the rancour has abated, in part perhaps because many of the principals originally involved in these discussions have disappeared from the scene.

The number of major mining operations still owned by investors from industrialized countries and situated in developing countries has been reduced. Hence, there will be fewer expropriations or forced transfers in the future. Moreover, governments that were attracted to public ownership of mineral operations during the era of expanding consumption and remunerative prices are now more cognizant of the hazards of the mineral markets. For many governments their state mining enterprises have been financial disasters.

Thus, increasingly, market-economy governments are likely to look with favour on joint ventures with private sector concerns for the operation of their mining industries. In countries with strong mining traditions and some domestic capital resources, the partners are likely to be local entrepreneurs. However, other countries with limited mining experience and inadequate capital resources will have to look to expatriate mining concerns as potential partners. In such undertakings, mutual respect and trust between partners is an essential ingredient to a successful undertaking. Differences of opinion are inevitable between the parties to a joint venture but a tolerant understanding of an opposing viewpoint can be helpful in overcoming difficulties. The Ok Tedi experience during the project's early stages is a case in point.

For the future, a possible area of conflict between governments is in the field of mineral trade. Developing countries promoting internal industrialization decry any barriers to the export of their goods to the industrialized countries. At the same time, to protect their infant industries, they adopt measures to limit imports. This double standard, while involving an apparent inconsistency, is nevertheless both understandable and not without parallel in the early histories and even current practices of some of the countries now industrialized, including the United States and Japan.

A useful outlet for the discussion of mineral trade issues has been the development of international organizations such as the International Lead-Zinc Study Group, which is under the aegis of the United Nations. These organizations are not to be confused with commodity agreement organizations. They make no attempt to govern prices, production or trade. Through meetings their purpose is to provide a vehicle for periodic discussions (normally once a year) of trends in commodity supply and demand by the government officials of the countries interested in the commodity. Industry representatives attend as advisors to government officials.

In this atmosphere problems that might otherwise develop into contentious issues can be objectively appraised and views can be exchanged. Statistical information is also compiled and distributed by the study groups, based on data submitted by the member governments. Several centrally-planned governments participate, but some (including the Soviet Union) do not submit statistics.

Efforts to Expand Trade Volumes

An increase in world trade is widely perceived as a means of lessening international tensions. Diplomats believe that by breaking down trade barriers ideological differences can be reduced and world peace promoted. In particular they believe that commerce provides a way to improve relations between the Soviet Union and the United States.

But these hopes run counter to a fundamental aspect of central planning. Even apart from issues of military security, countries committed to central planning will not participate in a truly 'open' economy in which trade is determined by market forces. Their planned economies require total control to survive.

Consequently, in looking at markets for minerals, producers in the market-economy countries cannot count on free sales access to the centrally-planned nations. This must be recognized by developing nations that believe they are entitled to an appropriate share of the world market.

An example is Chile's place in the world copper market. Spokesmen for the Chilean copper industry frequently have cited the fact that they possess perhaps one quarter of the known world copper reserves. They feel they are entitled to a corresponding share of the market. Yet their sales to the planned economies are minimal.

In 1984 the centrally-planned countries as a group produced 2·34 million tons of refined copper. That year, these countries imported 194,200 tons of refined copper from market-economy countries, offset by their own exports to the market-economy countries of 175,900 tons. Taking consumption as the sum of production plus imports minus exports, the centrally-planned countries used 2·36 million tons of copper in 1984. Chile's exports to these countries in 1984 were only 38,500 tons. Its market share in the centrally-planned countries was 1·5%, not 25%.

Poland, a major copper producer among the centrally-planned countries, has an output less than a third of Chile's, yet it exported 122,600 tons to market-economy nations, more than three times the amount Chile shipped to centrally-planned countries. The differences in trade access between the market-economy and the centrally-planned countries is striking, particularly when one considers that Chile is believed to be the world's lowest cost copper producer.

Multilateral trade negotiations are carried on at periodic intervals by the market-economy nations through the General Agreements for

Trade and Tariffs (GATT). The stated objective is to promote world commerce by reducing trade barriers. The goal is to ensure that goods are produced from the lowest cost, most efficient sources. This has not been, and is unlikely to become, the criterion for trade by the centrally-planned countries as a group.

Over the balance of the century, mineral producers in market-economy countries can expect to sell to centrally-planned countries only those quantities that their governments consider indispensable to the functioning of their economies. As for exports by centrally-planned countries to the market-economy countries, this volume will be determined by currency considerations. Internal costs of production will not play a significant role in influencing export decisions of the centrally-planned countries.

In Conclusion

What conclusions regarding the future can be drawn from this overview of the posture of the non-fuel minerals industry in the mid-eighties? The following appear to be the principal elements.

Demand — To the year 2000 the use of minerals will grow more slowly than the rate experienced in the third quarter of the century. The lag in demand for metals will be more pronounced than for non-metallics. Metals face formidable competition from composite materials and ceramics in many applications. Nevertheless, some modest expansion can be expected. Non-metallics enjoy well defined markets that they should be able to retain since low prices create little incentive to consumers to try substitutes.

Supply — Advances in the technology of exploration can be expected to lead to the discovery of abundant supplies of most major minerals for many years to come. Environmental limitations and higher costs will impinge on producers in the populous industrialized countries which will therefore lose market share to mineral operations in the emerging developing nations — a trend already well underway.

Costs — Improvements in the technologies used in extracting and processing minerals can be expected to keep costs of producing mineral commodities within bounds. Inflation that leads to depreciation of currency values may mask the real successes in cost control that the industry is almost certain to achieve in the future as it has in the past.

Prices — Despite efforts to achieve stability, mineral prices will continue to be highly volatile. However, the fluctuations will remain within the ranges that have prevailed since World War II for the major minerals, after adjusting for inflation. To the extent that supplies continue to be relatively inflexible in the face of volatile cyclical demand, the problem of price-depressing burdensome inventories will continue to plague minerals producers — particularly producers of metals.

Trade — An increase in minerals trade between market-economy and centrally-planned countries might do much to promote economic growth and improved international relations. However, such a development appears unlikely since open markets are not consistent with rigid state control of the economy as practised in the centrally-planned countries. Thus, the chance for an increase in mineral trade lies primarily within the market-economy nations. Research and market development is a possible tool for expanding consumption but the overriding factor is, of course, the state of the world economy.

Investments — Given price, political, technological and economic uncertainties, financing of mining ventures will remain a risky proposition. Whether private sector or state controlled, mineral enterprises can only secure access to sources of capital if they conduct themselves in a manner that engenders satisfactory credit ratings. Observance of contractual obligations will continue to be essential.

In the years ahead the mineral industries will have to accommodate themselves to the constantly shifting priorities of governments and the general public. Today the principal agreed goals appear to be:

Tranquil relationships among nations.

Improvement in world living standards, including better health care and education as well as adequate food, shelter and clothing.

Protection of the environment.

Conservation of non-renewable resources so that future generations will have access to adequate supplies of minerals.

Free and open trade, at least among the market-economy countries.

Each objective appears highly desirable but measures taken to implement one may cause problems in realizing another. Sometimes it may be necessary to modify one objective so that another objective can be attained. Two examples come to mind.

To protect the environment, stringent rules have been adopted governing the operation of processing plants recycling lead scrap. Because many of these operations are in the hands of small inadequately financed concerns that lack the capital to invest in pollution control devices, they have closed. A study made for the United States Environmental Protection Agency concluded that over a 10-year period as many as 120 million spent lead storage batteries would be discarded as waste instead of being recycled because of inadequate processing capacity. Not only would these constitute a hazard to health by being added to waste-dump sites, but some 1·2 million tons of lead would be irretrievably lost. Thus, environmental regulations would in effect defeat conservation objectives.

In the same way, free and open trade in minerals may cause the loss of mineral reserves by forcing some mines to close in a manner that will inhibit future recovery of their remaining reserves. This appears to be likely in the case of some of the high cost copper mines that have closed in North America since 1980. Obviously this is a loss for the distant future — since, as frequently stated in this text, existing reserves are adequate to supply mankind's needs for many years to come. But over the long-run, the intermittent operation of some mineral deposits as a consequence of market forces will mean the irretrievable loss of a share of total mineral reserves.

Thus, policy makers have to face up to the need to make choices. What concerns the managements of many mineral enterprises is that all too often government officials decide on courses of action to achieve one objective without sufficiently analyzing the side-effects their, decisions may have on other, perhaps equally desirable, objectives. Realities are seldom clearly divided between black and white. In most cases one has to select between various shades of grey.

A certain forecast one can make about the future of the mineral kingdom is that it will continue to experience change. Unforeseen events will influence the future course of markets, just as they have profoundly affected the experiences of the past. *To survive, mineral enterprises must be prepared to adapt to change.*

Index